The Complete Encyclopedia of Plants

An In-Depth Guide to Plant Care and Identification

CHRISTO KRAMER

Table of Contents

Introduction:

Plants rock! They are the coolest, most underappreciated life forms on this planet. Without plants, we wouldn't have oxygen to breathe, food to eat, wood to build our homes, medicine to cure diseases, or pretty flowers to gaze at. Let's face it, a world without plants would suck—big time.

I'm so excited to share the wonders of the plant kingdom with fellow plant lovers worldwide! My goal is to explore the diversity of plants in an informal, conversational way that makes you excited to learn. I won't bore you with overly technical botany terminology or exhaustive lists of plant species. Instead, I'll focus on unlocking the mysteries of how plants grow, adapt, and amaze us.

In these pages, we'll travel the globe together, stopping to smell the roses along the way. We'll marvel at thousand-year-old redwoods, dive into steamy jungles to discover orchids and wander deserts dotted with prickly cacti. We'll uncover secrets behind carnivorous plants that munch on insects and find out how seaweed thrives underwater. As we peek beneath the pot, even humble houseplants will seem new and exciting.

We'll dig into the diversity of the major plant groups, learning how each adapted to fill different ecological niches. We'll meet the ancient conifers, explore the variety of eye-catching flowering plants, hang with fungi's funky cousins, the ferns, and get prickly with cacti. We'll see how plants spread to cover the planet, colonizing the driest deserts and wettest rainforests. Then, we'll bring it home with tips for growing perfect houseplants and gorgeous gardens. We'll even get our hands dirty. Tackling fun DIY plant crafts, anyone can do.

Scientifically speaking, plants are complex organisms in the kingdom Plantae. These AMAZING creatures harness the sun's energy to make their own food via photosynthesis. Basically, they're solar-powered food factories using sunlight, water, and carbon dioxide to produce sugars and oxygen. How cool is that? This process feeds plants as well as gives US oxygen to breathe. Talk about a win-win situation!

Photosynthesis sets plants apart from other forms of life and allows them to thrive on land and in water. Thanks to their sun-catching skills, plants spread across the globe, diversifying into new species along the way. Today, there are over 300,000 types of plants, ranging from ancient conifers to flashy tropical flowers. We rely on this diversity for food, shelter, medicine, and overall well-being. Our whole WORLD depends on plants. Still, most of us take them for granted on a daily basis.

This book will be your gateway into the spectacular plant kingdom, taking you on an up-close tour of fern forests, cactus gardens, rainforest canopies, and more. We'll uncover the secrets of how plants work, find astonishing examples from every corner of the globe, and learn easy ways to bring more plants into our everyday lives.

Each chapter highlights stunning examples from the plant world, always with an eye toward conservation. As amazing as plants are, many are at risk due to human activities like deforestation and climate change. We'll shed light on endangered species and talk about ways we can help protect plants for the future. This is important stuff, but we'll learn it together in a way that inspires action, not despair.

Plants make the world beautiful, inside and out. Getting to know them will provide a newfound appreciation for your windowsill garden or even the trees in the park. My goal is to share my passion for plants with you on each page, getting us both pumped about botany.

Chapter 1

Introduction to the Plant Kingdom

The Evolution and Diversity of Plants

Plants are one of the most diverse, adaptable, and ubiquitous groups of organisms on Earth. The plant kingdom is a breathtaking testament to biodiversity, from towering redwoods in ancient forests to delicate mosses clinging to boulders. This tremendous diversity is the result of over a billion years of evolutionary tinkering, as plants adapted to fill virtually every terrestrial and aquatic habitat on the planet.

Most scientists believe plants e evolved from green algal ancestors sometime between 700-450 million years ago. Unlike their water-bound algal progenitors, early terrestrial plants developed complex biological innovations that allowed them to survive and reproduce on land. They evolved methods to transport water and nutrients efficiently without a surrounding aquatic environment. Protective waxy cuticles and structural compounds like lignin helped prevent water loss and provide structural integrity. Alternation of generations and spore dispersal achieved reproduction in the terrestrial realm.

As plants adapted to life on land over the ensuing millennia, they diversified into myriad forms. One of the earliest divisions in plant evolution separates the non-seed plants, such as mosses, liverworts, and ferns, from the seed plants, which include conifers, cycads, and flowering plants. Seed plants were an evolutionary innovation that allowed encased embryos and nutrients to survive away from water until conditions were right for germination. This advantage allowed seed plants to colonize drier habitats.

Within the seed plants, gymnosperms like conifers reproduce using exposed seeds, while angiosperms or flowering plants enclose seeds in protective fruit structures. Flowering plants dominate most terrestrial habitats, evolving specialized relationships with animal pollinators and dispersal agents. The rise of angiosperms fostered a burst of co-evolution and interdependency between plants and animals.

Today, taxonomists recognize over 300,000 species of plants, encompassing hundreds of families. However, new species continue to be identified, especially in biodiverse tropical regions. Plants display a mind-boggling array of different growth forms, reproductive mechanisms, and specialized metabolic compounds. From minute, floating duckweeds to complex, giant redwood forests, plants provide the foundation for virtually all terrestrial and freshwater ecosystems on the planet. Humans rely on plants for food, medicine, materials, aesthetic enjoyment, and much more. Our species owes plants an enormous debt of gratitude.
This botanical diversity is a testament to the flexibility and adaptability of the plant kingdom. Over countless eons, plants evolved solutions to the challenges of life on land, multiplying into new lineages and niches. The staggering variety of the plant kingdoms we observe today reveals their evolutionary success. As this book will explore, plant life displays many marvels, from intricate microscopic structures to complex interactions with other organisms. There are always new wonders to uncover in the diverse, dynamic, and ancient plant world. While plants may seem passive and immobile to the casual observer, they are highly dynamic living organisms. Like all life forms, plants require certain functions and structures to survive, grow and reproduce. Over evolutionary timescales, plants evolved specialized cells, tissues, and organs to meet their biological needs in the terrestrial environment. Understanding the physiology and morphology of plants provides crucial insight into how these diverse organisms operate and thrive.

At a cellular level, plant cells contain standard organelles such as nuclei, mitochondria, and vacuoles. But plants also developed distinctive cell types and structures. Photosynthetic chloroplasts allow plants to convert sunlight into chemical energy. Cell walls provide structural support and are made of tough compounds like cellulose. Many plant cells also contain large central vacuoles to store water and maintain turgor pressure against the cell wall. Different types of plant tissues organize cells into functional groups: dermal, vascular, ground, and meristematic tissues carry out particular roles.

Plants use specialized directional growth patterns and structures to orient their photosynthetic organs properly. Shoots exhibit negative gravitropism, growing upward toward sunlight. Roots display positive gravitropism, extending downward into the soil to absorb nutrients and water. This pattern of shoot and root systems establishes the basic form of vascular plants. Modified shoots like stems provide vertical structure and sites for leaves and reproductive organs. Root systems anchor the plant while mining the soil for resources.

Plants lack muscles and mobility, so they require other methods to transport water, sugars, and nutrients around their bodies. The plant vascular system of the xylem and phloem tissues enables this internal circulation. The xylem moves water and minerals from the roots upward through the shoot system. Phloem transports sugars and organic compounds in any direction, distributing energy and nutrients. This vascular pipeline allows plants to shuttle resources efficiently, even over long distances.

Flowering plants display particularly sophisticated physiology and development. Their root, shoot, leaf, vascular, and reproductive systems are fine-tuned for optimal growth and success. Phenomena like phototropism and circadian rhythms rely on complex signaling between plant tissues. Plants may seem passive, but use dynamic internal control systems to adapt, develop, and thrive. Their elegant biological solutions are an inspiration for science and technology.

Plants' stoic nature hides their vibrant inner lives. Their specialized cells, tissues, and organs overcome the challenges of a sessile, photosynthetic lifestyle. Studying the physiology of the plant kingdom reveals sophisticated biological innovations perfected over eons of evolution. Their dynamic structures and functions enable plants to survive, adapt, and proliferate across the globe. Even the most humble weed is a marvel of biological engineering on the cellular scale.

Plant Biology and Physiology

Plants are complex, fascinating organisms that have adapted over millions of years to thrive in a wide range of environments on land. To understand the diversity of the plant kingdom, it is essential to grasp the underlying biology and physiology that enables plants to grow, develop, and reproduce. This chapter will provide an in-depth look at the inner workings of plants and the special structures and processes that allow them to survive.

Unlike animals, plants are sessile, meaning they are stationary. This sedentary lifestyle requires special adaptations. Most plants have bodies composed of shoots and roots. The shoot system contains stems, leaves, flowers, and cones. This above-ground structure absorbs light energy and CO2 from the air to manufacture food via photosynthesis. The root system anchors the plant while absorbing water and minerals from the soil. Roots also store food reserves underground.

Vascular tissue composed of xylem and phloem vessels runs throughout the plant body, forming a continuous network to transport water, nutrients, and sugars between the shoots and roots. Water Evapotranspiration from the leaves pulls water up from the roots. The clever capillary action, cohesion, and transpiration physics create a suction force that defies gravity to deliver water through slender tubes to heights over 100 meters in the tallest trees.

The outer boundary of the plant body is covered in a waxy cuticle layer made of cutin and wax. This waterproof coating prevents desiccation while allowing gas exchange through tiny pores called stomata. Specialized guard cells open and close the stomatal pores to regulate this gas exchange. In a process called transpiration, stomata release water vapor from the moist inner leaf, which pulls up more water from the roots.

Botanists classify plant structures based on the presence or absence of specialized vascular tissue. Nonvascular plants like mosses lack these water-conducting cells. Vascular plants contain xylem and phloem, including ferns, conifers, and flowering plants. Vascularization was a pivotal adaptation that enabled plants to grow taller and transport water and nutrients longer distances.

The rigid cell walls of plants are built from cellulose fibers bonded with lignin and pectin. These complex carbohydrate polymers provide structural support against gravity and the pull of turgor pressure from the water, filling each living plant cell. Plants generate energy through photosynthesis in organelles called chloroplasts, which contain the green pigment chlorophyll. This amazing molecule harnesses light energy to convert CO_2 into glucose sugars.
One of the hallmarks of plants is their developmental plasticity. Unlike animals, plants maintain pools of undifferentiated stem cells throughout their lives. This allows them to continue growing, forming new organs and tissues as needed. Botanists classify grasses as monocots, having one seed leaf, and most other flowering plants as eudicots with two seed leaves. These major groups have key differences in anatomy, including leaf vein patterns, pollen, and flower parts.
. As we thoroughly survey the major groups of plants throughout this book, we will unpack more about the clever evolutionary adaptations that allow them to grow, develop, and reproduce in myriad environments. A deep understanding of what makes plants tick internally reveals the amazing diversity we see across the plant kingdom. Reproduction is key to the success and diversity of the plant kingdom. Plants have complex life cycles with alternating generations between diploid (2N) sporophytes and haploid (N) gametophytes. This enables genetic recombination during sexual reproduction, allowing populations to adapt.

Flowering plants reproduce through pollination, fertilization, and seed dispersal. Pollen grains containing sperm cells are transferred from the anther to the stigma. The pollen tube grows down the style to deliver sperm to the ovules. Double fertilization occurs as one sperm fertilizes the egg to become a diploid zygote while a second sperm joins the central cell nuclei to produce triploid endosperm tissue. This provides food reserves for the embryo as the seed develops.

Botanists classify flowering plants into monocots and eudicots based on embryo differences. Monocot embryos have one cotyledon or seed leaf, while eudicots have two. This divergence traces back 200 million years to the ancestors of modern flowering plant lineages. Adaptive radiation gave rise to astonishing diversity as flowering plants dominated most terrestrial ecosystems.

Flower morphology also differs between monocots and eudicots. Monocot flower parts occur in multiples of three, while eudicots have flower organs arranged in fours or fives. Examples include trillium flowers with three petals versus roses with five. Flowers attract pollinators like insects, birds, and bats to transfer pollen between plants. This coevolution shaped the dizzying array of flower forms, colors, and scents across plant families.

Plants also reproduce asexually through vegetative propagation. Horizontal stems like stolons and rhizomes allow plants to spread clones of themselves. Many plants readily regenerate from fragments like stem cuttings or root sections. This cloning from plant parts underlies the horticultural propagation of popular cultivars. Plants like strawberries send out runners with daughter plants genetically identical to the parent.

Of course, sexual reproduction shuffling genes remains key for evolutionary adaptation. Some plants display sexual dimorphism with separate male and female plants, like willows and poplars, which have dangling catkins bearing either pollen or ovules. Other species, like oaks, carry both male and female flowers on the same plant.

Plant genomes can be shockingly complex. The Paris japonica plant was found to have a whopping 149 pairs of chromosomes, over 50 times more than humans! Recent studies also discovered rampant polyploidy, with whole genome duplications in the ancestry of many plants like potatoes, coffee, bananas, and strawberries. This genomic redundancy provides the raw material for evolution.

Plants display amazing developmental plasticity modulated by phytohormones like auxins, cytokinins, and gibberellins. Growth patterns respond dynamically to the environment. Phototropism turns leaves toward light via auxin gradients, while gravitropism makes roots grow downwards using statoliths sensing gravity. Plants integrate complex inputs to optimize growth and reproduction.

This brief survey reveals how the biology and physiology of plants underlie their incredible diversity. Photosynthesis, vascular tissue, specialized structures like roots and leaves, complex life cycles, reproductive strategies, and genomic flexibility all contribute to the success of plants in adapting to fill nearly every terrestrial niche. As botanical explorers, the more we learn about what makes plants tick, the more we can appreciate the natural wonders of the plant kingdom.

Ecology and Habitats of Plants

Plants thrive in a remarkable range of habitats across different extremes of climate, elevation, soil types, and environmental conditions worldwide. Understanding the ecology of plants and their adaptations to specific environments helps us appreciate the diversity of the plant kingdom. This chapter explores key habitats and plant communities shaped by climate, geography, and other ecological factors.

The three main climate zones – tropical, temperate, and boreal – each support distinctive types of vegetation adapted to conditions like rainfall, temperatures, and length of growing season. Tropical zones have no frost, with year-round warmth and high precipitation. Dense rainforests teem with diversity, including majestic broadleaf evergreen trees, colorful flowering plants, epiphytes, and vines.

Temperate zones have seasonal changes with warm summers and cold winters. Moderate rainfall patterns support forests dominated by deciduous trees like oaks, maples, and beeches that lose their leaves in winter. Grassland prairies and shrublands also occur in temperate climates. Boreal zones have long, frigid winters and short, cool summers. Narrow conifers like spruce, fir, pine, and larches with needle leaves are adapted to survive deep freezes and snow.

Within these broad climate regions, vegetation varies locally with geography. Elevation gradients create stacked zones of distinct plant communities. Mountains rising into alpine zones support tundra and fellfields above the treeline. Foothills house conifer forests transitioning to spruce-fir at higher elevations. Montane meadows occur in valleys with wildflowers and grasses responding to snowmelt moisture.

From marshy wetlands to fast-draining sandy soils, soil types also influence plant habitats. Unique plants occupy specialized edaphic environments like calcareous glades, gypsum outcrops, serpentine barrens, and salt marshes. Harsh conditions like salinity, alkalinity, or heavy metals select for endemic flora like salt pines and rare metallophytes found nowhere else.
Of course, the most recognized plant habitat is the rainforest. Lush tropical and temperate rainforests harbor astonishing biodiversity. Multiple canopy layers with emergent trees, closed canopy, and understory plants create vertical stratification. Epiphytes perch on branches, while vines and lianas twine up tree trunks. The damp forest floor houses mosses, ferns, and herbaceous plants.

Deserts present intense challenges for plants with scorching heat, bright sunlight, and limited water availability. Specialized xerophytic plants have adaptations like succulent tissues, waxy cuticles, water-storing stems, and deep roots to enhance water uptake and retention. Cacti and other desert flora thrive where rainfall is sparse.

Coastal habitats along seashores and salt marshes contain halophytic plants tolerant of saline soils and sea spray. Mangrove forests specialized with aerial roots and salt filtration inhabit tropical intertidal zones. Higher latitudes support salt marsh grasses, succulents, and shrubs adapted to sandy or muddy flats flooded by tides.

Each unique habitat across varying climate zones, geography, and soil environments supports specially adapted assemblages of native vegetation shaped by ecology and evolution. As botanists, observing plants in their natural habitats teaches us how different species are exquisitely tailored to thrive under diverse global growing conditions. Plant communities develop through ecological succession as new species populate areas over time. Pioneer species are established first in disturbed habitats like clearings or burned areas. Sun-loving annuals and perennials grow rapidly from windborne seeds and have short life cycles. Later, successional species emerge under shade from shrubs and young trees. Eventually, a stable climax community dominated by mature canopy trees takes shape after centuries.

Competition shapes plant communities as closely related species vie for resources like light, space, water, and soil nutrients. Niche partitioning reduces direct competition, for example, the tiered forest structure. Facilitation occurs when certain plants benefit neighbors, like nitrogen-fixing legumes enriching the soil.

Disturbance resets succession as fires, floods, avalanches, and windstorms destroy habitats. This engenders cycles of disturbance and recovery. Some plants depend on periodic fires to stimulate flowering, open gaps, or release seeds from pinecones. Habitats can transition between alternative stable states in shifting mosaics across the landscape.

Invasive plants disrupt native plant communities through unchecked growth and resource monopolization. Often lacking natural predators, invasive species spread aggressively, displacing diverse flora. Humans promote ecological balance through sustainable practices like selective harvesting, controlled burns, meadow mowing, and removing invasive species.
Botanists classify associated plants recurring together in communities as plant associations. These form recognizable habitat types like oak savannas or spruce-fir forests. Biogeography examines the distributions of plants and animals across varying geography and ecosystems—Floras catalog plant diversity for different regions.

Vegetation maps depict geographic zones of characteristic plant communities in landscapes. Ecoregions delineate areas defined by distinct ecological factors like climate, soils, landforms, and vegetation types. Biomes describe major regional habitat types like tundra, grasslands, deserts, or woodlands. Global patterns emerge, like circumpolar taiga and tundra biomes encircling subarctic latitudes.

Plant ecology provides key insights for conservation. Preserving high-diversity habitats protects vulnerable endemic flora. Restoration ecology repairs damaged ecosystems by reintroducing native species. Understanding ecological relationships in plant communities ensures sustainable management through enhancing biodiversity, regulating invasive pests, and promoting ecosystem health across changing landscapes.

As botanical explorers, observing the ebb and flow of ecology across varying ecosystems provides context to enrich our knowledge. Flowers make more sense after seeing prairies ablaze with color. Conifers resonate more when walking forests and smelling that piney fragrance. The sounds of birds and insects, dappled shade, and meadow scents fill out the experience. Habitats tell ecological stories layered with meaning to deepen our connection with plant communities worldwide.

The Importance of Plants for Humans

It is impossible to overstate the importance of plants for human civilizations throughout history and continuing today. Plants provide food, medicine, materials, fuels, ecosystem services, and inspiration, forming the foundation of agriculture, health, technology, culture, and aesthetics. Our language, traditions, economy, and future depend on plants.

Most obviously, plants provide nutrition for people. A dozen crop species – wheat, rice, maize, soybeans, and potatoes – supply over 70% of global dietary energy intake. Fruits, nuts, vegetables, beans, greens, herbs, and spices enrich our cuisine. Chocolate, coffee, tea, sugarcane, and hops provide flavor for popular beverages. Even livestock depend on plant forage like grasses, hay, and silage to ultimately nourish people through animal products like milk and eggs.

Medicinal uses of plants date to prehistory and remain vital today. Aspirin originated from willow bark. Foxglove gives digitalis for heart conditions. The antimalarial quinine comes from cinchona bark. Morphine, codeine, and related opioids relieve pain from poppy extracts. Plants provide antimicrobial, anticancer, and countless other bioactive compounds, making herbal medicine a global multibillion-dollar industry.

Plants generate fuels, fibers, wood, and myriad materials sustaining modern life—fossil fuels from ancient plants power civilization. Cotton, flax, hemp, and other plant fibers become textiles and rope. Lumber builds structures. Cellulose from plants makes paper, rayon, cellophane, and other products. Essential oils lend natural perfumes and flavorings. The list of goods originating from botanical materials seems endless.

Ecosystem services from plants support and protect life on Earth. Photosynthesis generates oxygen while absorbing carbon dioxide. Plants prevent soil erosion. Forests, grasslands, and wetlands filter water. Vegetation moderates climates locally and globally. Plants fertilize and stabilize landscapes, provide habitat, and form the foundation of food chains sustaining all life.
Cultural traditions worldwide link intimately with plants. Holidays showcase floral symbols like poinsettias, cherry blossoms, roses, or lilies. Trees often represent mythology, identity, and history, like the cedars of Lebanon. Rice in Asia, maize in the Americas, and the olive tree in Mediterranean regions all define regional cultures.

Plants and humans are symbiotically intertwined. Plants inspire art, poetry, prose, songs, and creative expression. New uses arise constantly. Problems like famine, disease, climate change, and environmental damage require botanical ingenuity for solutions. Present and future generations depend on the genius of the plant kingdom and those who decipher its secrets. The interdependence between plants and people has only deepened through history as civilizations harness plants more intensively for agriculture, technology, medicine, and culture. But this relationship also faces challenges requiring thoughtful stewardship.

Impacts from population growth, pollution, climate change, invasive pests, habitat loss, and other factors threaten plant biodiversity worldwide—overharvesting drives some species, like medicinal plants, toward extinction. Deforestation for timber and cropland destroys irreplaceable ecosystems.

Pesticide overuse poisons pollinators, soil, organisms, and beneficial plants. Invasive nonnative plants and pathogens disrupt communities. Climate shifts push species ranges outside historic niches. Environmental changes destabilize traditional agriculture and ethnobotany.
Conserving plants for sustainable use requires balancing increased harvesting with responsible practices to maintain healthy, biodiverse ecosystems. Holistic approaches integrate traditional knowledge and emerging science.

Agroecology applies ecological principles to grow food sustainably. Agroforestry combines trees with crop cultivation. Permaculture designs integrated plant communities modeled on nature for site-specific benefits. Conservation breeding protects rare, endemic plants, while seed banks preserve genetic diversity. Botanic gardens showcase and study plants. Creative solutions expand as problems arise.

Together, we can work to inspire future generations to continue to value plants through research, education, and encouraging eco-friendly behaviors like planting gardens using native species. Supporting botanical sciences expands beneficial applications. Well-crafted laws and agreements regulate destructive practices while encouraging stewardship. And the plants themselves demonstrate resilience. Given the smallest chance, grass pokes through cracks in concrete jungles. Conifers persist atop stark mountainsides. Seeds lying dormant for decades sprout when conditions allow. Novel genotypes emerge via mutations and gene flow. Plants adapt and evolve endlessly through cycles of change.

Our green planet fundamentally relies on the genius of plants. They feed, heal, shelter, clothe, inspire, and sustain civilizations.

This book endeavors to build knowledgeable plant enthusiasts equipped to support that future. Learn to identify important plants where you live—volunteer at natural areas and botanical institutions. Support science-backed organizations and ethical companies. Educate others and magnify meaningful actions through social networks. The personal becomes collective. Together, we can ensure plants thrive for generations to come.

Major Plant Groups

The plant kingdom encompasses astonishing diversity, with over 369,000 accepted species, including ferns, gymnosperms, flowering plants, and more. This chapter provides an introductory overview profiling distinctive plant groups highlighted in detail throughout the book. Understanding unique traits, evolutionary origins, and key families provides helpful context for appreciating the variety found across the botanical world.

Non-vascular plants lack specialized water and nutrient-conducting tissues and depend on passive uptake and transport. Liverworts, mosses, and hornworts comprise ancient bryophyte lineages over 400 million years old. Mosses form feathery or shrubby tufts on moist substrates. Liverworts grow flattened mats or rosettes on damp surfaces. Hornworts develop thin green tissue sheets. Despite the simple structure, bryophytes occupy diverse habitats globally.

Vascular plants possess xylem and phloem tissue, enabling efficient internal circulation. Lycophytes like clubmosses and spikemosses represent early vascular plants from 380 million years ago. Horsetails and whisk ferns showcase ancient lineages. Leptosporangiate ferns dominate today, with around 9000 species of graceful fronds decorating forest floors and margins worldwide.

Gymnosperms bear naked seeds on cones, a successful reproductive strategy that evolved over 300 million years ago. Conifers dominate extant gymnosperms with over 600 pines, firs, cedars, cypress species, and more. Ginkgo, cycads, gnetophytes, and others represent unique gymnosperm structures with restricted distributions. Conifer forests blanket northern latitudes.

Flowering plants form the most recent major plant radiation—angiosperm success results from insect pollination, fruits enclosing seeds, and rapid speciation. There are over 300,000 species of flowering plants divided into monocots and eudicots based on embryo structure. Popular monocots include grasses, orchids, palms, and gingers. Diverse eudicots encompass roses, sunflowers, legumes, oaks, and most other plants.

Flowers are similarly diverse, from showy petals attracting pollinators to minute, wind-pollinated blooms. Growth habits range from towering trees to tiny alpine wildflowers pollinated by flies. Adaptations equip flowering plants to thrive on every continent. Speciation and hybridization continue generating new forms.

Carnivorous plants use their jaw-like leaves to trap live prey. Diverse mechanisms power moist pitfall traps in pitcher plants, flypaper sticky leaves, and snap traps in Venus flytraps. Over 700 carnivorous plant species occur mostly in nutrient-poor bogs. Related plants use sticky secretions or pitfall traps to catch prey.

Succulents store water in fleshy tissues, allowing survival in arid habitats: spines, waxy skin, and CAM photosynthesis curb water loss. Cacti exemplify specialized succulents. Other succulents include agaves, aloes, jade plants, and numerous species that evolved in deserts worldwide—people prize succulents for unusual shapes and drought tolerance.

These profiles provide a taste of the major plant groups explored in this book. Trees, shrubs, herbaceous plants, grasses, sedges, rushes, and diverse other growth forms populate habitats globally. Unique traits equip plants for challenging environments, from mangrove vivipary to crucifer deterrence mechanisms. By understanding the hallmarks of key plant groups, we enrich the experience of exploring botanical diversity.

Aquatic plants thrive submerged in freshwater habitats like lakes, rivers, and ponds—diverse adaptations aid life in water, including underwater pollination and seed dispersal. Floating plants have leaves with waxy cuticles resting atop the surface. Emergent plants root underwater with erect aerial stems and leaves. Submerged plants grow entirely underwater. Mangroves flourish in salty intertidal zones.

Wetland plants tolerate waterlogged, oxygen-poor soils. Cattails, rushes, and sedges inhabit marshes. Carnivorous plants favor nutrient-poor bogs. Swamp forests grow trees adapted to wet soils like cypress and tupelo. Wetland plants filter runoff, reduce flooding, and provide habitat.

Parasitic plants steal nutrients and water from host plants via attachments like haustoria. Mistletoe taps into tree branches. Dodder entwines host stems. Rafflesia and corpse flowers lack leaves and chlorophyll, receiving all nutrition through fungal connections to tree roots while flowering briefly and attracting insect pollinators.

Algae provide essential aquatic habitats and food chains. Multicellular seaweeds like kelp thrive in marine environments, while freshwater relatives prefer lakes and streams. Phytoplankton drift through seas and lakes. Photosynthetic algal symbionts enable the success of corals and giant clams. Agar, carrageenan, and other algal products find human uses.

Fungi fill essential ecological roles as decomposers and symbionts. Mushrooms and other macrofungi break down organic matter. Lichens combine algae and/or cyanobacteria with fungal partners. Mycorrhizae trade nutrients with plant roots. Yeasts and other microfungi inhabit diverse microhabitats.

This book cannot do justice to the enormity of botanical diversity across all groups, from tiny phytoplankton to towering tree ferns. But by highlighting distinctive features, evolutionary origins, and key families, we build helpful frameworks to enrich enjoying plants in their astounding variety. Observe keenly, question thoughtfully, and keep exploring the beautiful complexity of the plant kingdom.

Using This Book

This book endeavors to ignite a passion for the remarkable diversity of the plant kingdom.

Curiosity and patient observation are the botanist's greatest assets. AMMA is an acronym encapsulating core skills for using this book effectively:

Ask questions. Plants seem familiar, but each has an epic story shaping its existence.
Why is that leaf shaped so strangely? How does this species spread? Questioning focuses attention on details that are easy to overlook. Every plant offers mysteries to unravel. Stay curious.

Marvel. The deeper you look, the more wonders you discover. Leaves seem simple at first glance, but up close, their architecture astonishes. Think like Sherlock Holmes surveying plants for clues revealing hidden adaptations and relationships. Let yourself be amazed.

Make connections. How do form and function coexistin this plant? What similarities or differences occur compared to related species? Linking observations builds deeper understanding. Share discoveries to spark insights from others.

Appreciate beauty. From perfect symmetry to exuberant excess, plants exhibit artistic genius. Notice varied textures, graceful shapes, subtle shades, and intricate patterns. Let aesthetic sensitivity sharpen observation skills. Beauty and understanding are intertwined.
Start in your own backyard. Learn common local trees, shrubs, and wildflowers first. Carry a field guide or a notebook with you as you explore. Reach out to other botany enthusiasts in your area, either online or in person. If you're an artist, you may find that your journey into botany enriches your existing art practice in unexpected ways. You may find yourself writing a poem about a particular flower or drawing a particular plant in a still life.

Then, think about what green spaces you want to cultivate. Incorporate plants into your everyday life via a windowsill garden or even a simple succulent. Give back to local conservation efforts in your community, or join a community garden. Humans, like plants, are an interdependent species.

The chapters ahead are foundational. Use them as a catalyst to ignite your own curiosity.

Chapter 2
Ferns and Fern Allies

Features of Ferns

Ferns are ancient vascular plants that dominated forest ecosystems for millennia before flowering plants. Today, over 12,000 living fern species inhabit diverse habitats across the globe. Ferns may appear primitive and delicate, yet they possess remarkable adaptations enabling their evolutionary success. The most recognizable feature of ferns is the frond – an expansive, divided leaf composed of a photosynthetic blade attached to a stipe stem-like structure. Fronds exhibit astonishing diversity in forms, ranging from simple elliptical shapes to intricately frilled plumes several meters long. Depending on the species, the blade may be entire or variously lobed and segmented.

.

Fern leaves lack flowers and seeds. Instead, sporangia develop on the undersides of fronds, usually arranged in clusters called sori. Each sporangium produces haploid spores by meiosis that later develop into free-living, heart-shaped gametophytes that produce eggs and sperm. This alternation of generations characterizes the fern life cycle.

Ferns possess vascular tissue – xylem and phloem – for circulating water and nutrients internally. However, water transport relies on primitive tracheids rather than more advanced vessels that evolved later in flowering plants. Rhizomes, stolons, and other root-like structures anchor ferns while branching underground to spread the plant vegetatively.

A waxy cuticle covers fern fronds to prevent desiccation. Stomata allow gas exchange for photosynthesis. Patterns like indumentum hairs minimize water loss while admitting light. Cell growth localized at meristems enables indeterminate fern growth to maximize leaf area as needed. Some epiphytic ferns have specialized tissues for absorbing moisture.

Ferns thrive in shaded forest understories where their expansive fronds can intercept stray flecks of sunlight filtered through the canopy above. Plentiful moisture also favors ferns. Those adapted to drier areas often have thick or waxy fronds, inrolled margins to reduce air exposure, or hairy scales limiting water loss.

Various defensive strategies protect ferns from herbivores. Toxins like phenols may accumulate in tissues unpalatable to grazers while providing pigments, causing distinctive dark frond coloration. Physical or chemical deterrents even defend vulnerable reproductive sori from insects, slugs, and snails.

While anatomically simple, ferns have evolved manifold adaptations, enabling their persistence over 175 million years across diverse habitats, from steamy tropical rainforests to cold temperate woodlands. Their unique morphology and growth reflect solutions to challenges, including reproduction, water transport, light capture, herbivory, and decay.
Ferns exhibit fascinating adaptations tailored to their environments. Epiphytic ferns growing on trees have specialized tissues for absorbing moisture and nutrients. The lip fern Chelianthes has glandular hairs secreting waxy droplets that magnify ambient light to aid photosynthesis in the shade.

Some ferns form symbioses with cyanobacteria or fungi. The photobiont layer on certain tropical fern leaves provides supplemental nutrition through nitrogen fixation and carbon compounds. Mycorrhizal associations between fern roots and fungal partners facilitate nutrient and water absorption.

Various physical and chemical defenses protect against herbivores. Prickles on some fronds deter larger grazers. Toxic or foul-tasting organic compounds accumulate in the tissues of certain ferns. The bracken fern produces carcinogenic substances and proteinase inhibitors.
Many ferns spread rapidly by rhizomes, and crowded clones compete aggressively for space and light. Temperate sword fern groves expand relentlessly by subterranean runners. Certain tropical ferns like Dicranopteris Curvehog actually deploys allelopathic secretions hindering neighboring plants.

Of course, the paramount adaptations of ferns relate to reproduction by spores. This strategy evolved early in Earth's history when drying land conditions favored airborne dispersal over motile waterborne sperm. Each wind-blown fern spore represents a genetically unique haploid gametophyte potential, allowing great variability.

Some ferns have evolved over time, using hybridization to create new species, such as the hundreds of maidenhair fern crosses. Apogamy enables certain ferns to bypass sexual reproduction, with sporophytes generating new diploid sporophytes directly.

The ostrich fern Matteuccia offers a model of fern reproductive ingenuity. Separate fertile and sterile fronds maximize both photosynthesis and spore distribution. Sporangia eject spores explosively to spread genetic material widely. And unlike most ferns, Matteuccia is nontoxic and actually edible!

Ferns have thrived for eons by elegantly adapting their graceful yet simple morphology and physiology to challenges across the globe. While often considered relics today, celebrating their diverse adaptations affirms that ferns remain dynamic and evolving survivors.

Fern Life Cycles and Reproduction

Ferns exhibit a unique life cycle characterized by the alternation of generations between diploid sporophytes that produce haploid spores and free-living gametophytes that generate eggs and sperm. This intricate reproductive strategy evolved early among vascular plants as an adaptation to survive on dry land using spores for dispersal. Understanding fern life cycles provides insight into the success of these diverse primitive plants.

The familiar leafy fern we see is the sporophyte plant. Meiosis occurs within sporangia, usually clustered into sori on the undersides of fern fronds. Each sporangium forms around 48 haploid spores that disperse widely on the wind before germinating to grow into a small, flattened, independent gametophyte.

The gametophyte or prothallus is heart-shaped and just a few millimeters wide, often green but lacking vascular tissue. Motile sperm must swim via surface moisture to fertilize the egg retained on the gametophyte. The resulting diploid zygote grows into a new sporophyte plant by mitosis, completing the fern life cycle.

There are variations on this pattern. Some derived ferns exhibit apogamy, where certain gametophyte cells grow directly into sporophytes without fertilization. Hybridization also occurs between related fern species, enabling novel genetic recombinations as new sporophytes inherit genes from two parents.

Fern gametophytes exhibit several adaptations to increase reproductive success. Chemical attraction cues guide swimming sperm. Structural variations allow either self-fertilization or outcrossing between separate male and female gametophytes. Many gametophytes are photosynthetic, while some obtain nutrients from mycorrhizal fungal partners.

The independent gametophyte stage confers several advantages. Each unique haploid gametophyte generated from meiotic spores introduces genetic variety. Small gametophyte size allows reproduction in marginal habitats. Fertilization requires external water for sperm motility, selecting for humid environments. And diploid sporophytes benefit from fused genomes.

In fact, the prominence of diploid dominance in the fern life cycle illustrates a pivotal transition in plant evolution. Whereas in algae and bryophytes, the gametophyte is the prominent photosynthetic phase, the sporophyte became dominant in ferns, enabling them to grow much larger by mitosis and occupy diverse forest niches as vascularity developed.

The intricacies of fern life cycles belie their archaic origins, dating back over 300 million years. The alternation of generations conferred key advantages that enabled primitive ferns to flourish across habitats where their descendants still thrive today. Observing a tiny heart-shaped gametophyte sprouting in the wild amidst towering diploid fronds inspires awe at the continuity of this ancient botanical heritage. The fern life cycle includes a simple independent gametophyte just a few cells thick, yet it controls a key transition point determining sporophyte genetics. Tiny haploid prothalli harbor remarkable developmental potential. Observing fertile fronds release clouds of ancient spores harkens to primordial forests.

Another unusual facet of fern reproduction is that new sporophytes often germinate directly atop the parent gametophyte. The juvenile fiddleheads emerge already anchored to the ground and able to begin photosynthesizing, circumventing the delicate and dangerous stage of spore dispersal.

Ferns combine primitive traits like spore dispersal with advanced strategies like epiphytism. Their resilience over hundreds of millions of years reflects such flexible adaptability. Some evolutionary biologists categorize ferns as "hopeful monsters" – organisms trying creative new genetic combinations that may spawn future lineages.

Indeed, both seed plants and flowering plants likely descended from fern-like ancestors. Botanists hypothesize that seed cone structures originated when certain prothalli began partly enclosing developing sporophytes. Flowers and enclosed seeds evolved as gametophytes further protected zygotes, allowing colonization of drier habitats.

Threats from habitat loss make proactive fern conservation important. Fortunately, many fern species resist inbreeding depression through sporophyte self-incompatibility factors. Spore banks in soils and existing populations provide reservoirs of genetic diversity. Rampant hybridization generates adaptive new genotypes. Ferns continue to evolve with protected habitats, exhibiting nature's creativity through evolutionary time.

Notable Fern Families

With over 12,000 diverse species, ferns have evolved into various family groups with unique features, adapting them to thrive in habitats across the globe. Gaining familiarity with distinctive fern families provides helpful guidelines for identification while revealing fascinating facets of fern diversity. From dainty filmy ferns to towering tree ferns, each family expands our botanical appreciation.

The Osmundaceae family contains some of the most primitive living ferns. Royal fern and cinnamon fern display large, dramatic fronds. The genus Osmunda gives the family its name. Globally distributed, these moisture-loving ferns often grow along streams and in bogs. Their fertile fronds turn nutritious due to starch storage, making some edible.

The Hymenophyllaceae, or filmy fern family, encompasses over 600 epiphytic species adapted to humid rainforests. Their thin translucent fronds have just a single cell layer for efficient gas exchange. Filmy ferns lack cuticles to absorb moisture from constantly wet tree trunks and branches where they grow. Other epiphytic families include the grammitid ferns and vittarioid ferns.

The unique Schizaeaceae family contains the unusual curly grass and comb ferns found in subtropical and tropical regions. Their narrow segmented fronds unfurl into wiry spirals. While the foliage appears grass-like, the sori identifies them as ferns. Some species are spread by underground rhizomes forming large mats.

The common bracken fern genus Pteridium represents the Dennstaedtiaceae family of ferns. Worldwide distribution makes brackens the most abundant ferns. Potentially spreading over 20 feet (6 m) across bracken rhizome networks accumulate toxic compounds, deterring grazers. Concerns about invasiveness exist in certain areas.

The wood fern family Dryopteridaceae contains over 1,700 species, including popular oak ferns and wood ferns. Male fern was used historically to control tapeworms. Dryopteridaceae species thrive in temperate forests across North America, Eurasia, and northern Latin America. Frond shapes often resemble maple leaves.

The Polypodiaceae, or common polypody family, encompasses over 1,200 tropical, subtropical, and temperate fern species. This family includes the popular ornamental polypody ferns with thin lacy fronds. Maidenhair ferns belong here, too, with delicate doubly compound foliage. The long rhizomes of polypody ferns allow them to spread readily in moist forests.

The adder's-tongue family Ophioglossaceae has just one genus – Ophioglossum, the adder's tongues. These primitive ferns Inhabit damp soils worldwide and have a single frond divided into sterile and fertile portions. The sporangia form a spike resembling a small tongue. Unusual Botrychium ferns in the related Botrychium genus have mosaic-like sterile fronds. Marsileaceae's aquatic fern family contains unusual ferns adapted to wetlands and damp soils. They produce four-parted clover-like foliage, unlike typical fern fronds. Sporocarps with internal sori rather than exposed ones aid reproduction underwater.

Tree ferns comprise the Cyatheaceae family, with massive trunks supporting a crown of arching fronds. Scaly hairs protect the trunks. Found in tropical and subtropical forests worldwide, tree ferns can exceed 66 feet (20 m) in height! Tree ferns defined coal-age Jurassic landscapes.
The Pteridaceae family or brake fern family contains over 1,000 species of cosmopolitan ferns. Some, like brake ferns, prefer shady understories, while others, like lip ferns, tolerate sun if moisture suffices. Their sporangia lack protective indusium coverings.

Finally, the Bereberidaceae family represents an ancient lineage dating back 350 million years with just two rare genera today – Anogramma and Psilotum. Species like Anogramma leptophylla have fronds adapted to hot, arid environments. The Psilotum exhibits primitive vascular tissue.

This brief survey reveals the diversity encompassed by distinct fern families, from towering tree ferns to tiny filmy ferns adapted to their various ecological niches. Exploring ferns by family provides a window into the evolutionary past, shedding light on successful adaptive strategies. Even the most delicate-looking fern displays resilient survivorship against geological ages.

Ferns as Houseplants

Ferns are graceful and delicate, which makes them ideal house plants. While some fern species better suit greenhouses, many adapt well to indoor cultivation.

Ferns naturally favor shaded, humid forests and thus require bright ambient light but not direct sun indoors. East or West-facing windows work well. Use sheer curtains to diffuse intense light. Rotate plants if sunlight exposure seems uneven. Provide supplemental fluorescent lighting if natural light seems inadequate.

Indoor ferns need consistently moist, loose, and well-draining soil high in organic matter. Water thoroughly whenever the top inch of soil dries out. Use pots with drainage holes and saucers to avoid soggy roots. Misting the leaves helps increase humidity. Grouping ferns together benefits humidity.

Fertilize actively growing ferns every 2-4 weeks during the growing season with balanced liquids formulated for ferns and tropical plants—dilute applications to half-strength. Cease feeding over winter when growth slows. Re-pot into fresh soil annually or whenever roots fill pots.

Select ferns compatible with typical indoor conditions. Boston fern with long arching fronds has endured generations as a houseplant. Kimberly Queen and Dallas ferns offer ruffly or divided leaves. The compact tassel fern tolerates low light well. Bird's nest ferns and staghorn ferns mount epiphytically.

With delicate lacy foliage, Maidenhair ferns grow best in a humid terrarium or greenhouse. Similarly, the giant sword fern favors a sheltered patio over indoor dryness. Cold-tolerant varieties of cinnamon fern and lady fern transition nicely outdoors.

Avoid plants showing brown frond tips, spots, or uncurling fiddleheads when choosing ferns. Seek vibrant green color without yellowing. Check for pests like scale insects, mealybugs, spider mites, or thrips. Select young plants, not rootbound.

Patience and attentive care help ferns thrive indoors. Remember to mist ferns often while providing filtered light and using well-draining soil. Ferns quickly show distress if conditions drop below optimal. With adjustments guided by the plant's needs, lush indoor fern displays become living works of botanical art. When ferns struggle indoors, assess growing conditions to determine causes. Brown, crispy leaf edges signify inadequate humidity. Yellowing fronds indicate too much light. Drooping fronds may reflect overwatering versus underwatering. Adjust care accordingly but gradually.

Indoor ferns require diligent attention but repay the effort with graceful beauty. Setting plants atop pebble trays adds humidity through evaporation. You can also grow miniature varieties like bulbils or maidenhair ferns in terrariums.

Rotate plants monthly so all sides receive equal light. Wash foliage periodically to remove dust or salts. Trim away dead fronds at their stems—Propagate ferns from divisions when overcrowded or to share offspring.

Choose tough, leathery polypody, sword, or autumn ferns for lower maintenance options. Their sturdy fronds tolerate some neglect—the staghorn fern Platycerium mounts on bark plaques. The wavy-tongued ladder brake fern, Pteris Ensiformis, cascades nicely from hanging pots.

Consider native ferns for temperate climates when cultivating outdoors. Christmas ferns and lady ferns thrive in shade gardens. Evergreen wood ferns work in rock gardens. Maidenhair spleenwort and common polypody suit alpine troughs. Experiment to find the hardiest ferns for your locale.

Gardening and Ornamental Ferns

Ferns have become increasingly popular as garden ornamental plants over the last few decades. Their lush, graceful fronds add beautiful texture and an exotic, tropical look to garden beds and borders. Ferns come in a wide range of shapes, sizes, and colors, allowing ample choice to complement any landscape design. Ferns can thrive and enhance gardens in many climate zones with proper selection, placement, and care.

When choosing ferns for ornamental gardening, gardeners should first consider their USDA hardiness zone to select varieties adapted to survive local winters. Most ferns thrive in humid environments and prefer shade, although some tolerate partial sun if shielded from hot afternoon rays. Small ferns such as maidenhair fern, lady fern, and polypody fern grow well in rock gardens, woodland gardens, or as accent plants. Larger ferns like ostrich, cinnamon, and Christmas can provide dramatic focal points and lush backdrop plantings. There are even a few varieties that tolerate drought and full sun exposure.

Woodland gardens dotted with hostas, astilbes, coral bells, and an assortment of ferns create a peaceful sanctuary and stunning display. Mixing textures and forms creates visual interest. Plant tall ostrich and cinnamon ferns as bold vertical elements among low, broad hostas and smaller ferns like Korean rock fern and holly fern. Add height with suspended staghorn ferns attached to moss-covered boards or tree trunks. Contrast the finely cut fronds of asparagus fern with wide, overlapping fronds of sibling fern: Scatter lacy polypody, maidenhair, and button ferns throughout as delicate accents.

Shaded borders also benefit from the whimsical look of ferns. Combine them with other shade-lovers like impatiens, begonias, caladiums, and coleus. Try lady fern and Japanese painted fern along with colorful variegated hostas. Let ostrich fern mingle with lush green and purple-leaved basils—Intersperse Japanese tassel fern with frilly parsley and dill. Just take care to water border plantings regularly since most ferns require consistently damp soil.
For additions to water features or wet areas, water-loving marsh ferns, royal ferns, and sensitive ferns thrive. Tuck them near pond edges, waterfall splash zones, rain gardens, irises, lobelias, and bottle gentian. Spiky water clover emerges from shallow water and resembles a delicate underwater fern. Floating Azolla forms a thick green mat resembling duckweed but is actually a tiny aquatic fern.

When incorporating ferns into garden designs, pay close attention to each variety's specific needs for optimal growth. While some tolerate sun and drought, most prefer shade and moist, rich soil high in organic matter. Shelter ferns from harsh winds, which will shred their fronds. Providing a site protected by trees, fences, or shrubs creates a welcoming environment. Well-amended soil encourages strong root growth. A 2-4 inch layer of shredded leaves, bark chips, or compost as mulch helps retain soil moisture and prevents soil from drying out.
Careful watering is key, especially for varieties that demand consistently damp conditions. Install irrigation or provide thorough weekly deep watering. Container plantings and hanging baskets also need vigilance to avoid drying out. Monitor for pests like scale, mites, and aphids and treat them promptly before they damage tender new fronds. Apply slow-release pellet fertilizer in early spring and again in midsummer. Divide congested rootballs and repot container plants periodically. Cut back yellowing or damaged fronds at the base of the plant.

Ferns can enhance any garden with proper selection, placement, and care. Their graceful forms, lush textures, and variety of colors and shapes allow creativity in designing eye-catching displays. Woodland gardens, shaded borders, accent groupings, and containers are some ways to highlight ornamental ferns' unique charm. A new interest in sustainable and eco-friendly landscaping has also sparked enthusiasm for ferns. Once established, these ancient plants thrive without excessive watering, chemical fertilizers, pesticides, or pruning. Their innate resilience suits them well for low-maintenance gardens. Select varieties carefully and provide suitable growing conditions initially, and ferns will gracefully adorn the garden for years.
Public gardens and conservatories also recognize the alluring effect of artistically displayed ferns. They arrange diverse varieties inside controlled environments to showcase a palette of colors, forms, and textures. Brilliant blue and silver-edged varieties of Japanese-painted ferns accent deep green maidenhair and ostrich ferns. Contrast fine, lacy lady ferns with bold, ruffled bird's nest ferns and giant sword ferns of the tropics. The Hawaiian Honolulu Botanical Garden and Asheville Botanical Garden in North Carolina contain inspiring fern displays worth modeling.

Some imaginative garden designers even use ferns in unique ways beyond traditional plantings. Constructing vertical living walls composed of ferns, mosses, and other shade plants transforms blank expanses into verdant displays. Hardy resurrection fern and polypody thrive on natural bark or fiber panels irrigated with drip systems or humidifiers. Cradling tree trunks and stumps in blankets of moss studded with tiny filmy ferns create whimsical woodland artworks. Even just a simple trellis or pole adorned with hanging basket ferns adds a touch of vibrancy to shady spots.

When choosing planting containers for ferns, select wide, shallow pots that maximize surface area compared to depth. Ferns have horizontally spreading shallow roots that benefit from broad, deep pots. Planting mixes should be loose, friable, and fast draining but hold some moisture. Pre-made fern and orchid mixes work well. Cover drainage holes with pebbles or small bits of broken pottery, and top-dresses with pine bark nuggets to help retain moisture while discouraging weeds.

Outdoor planted containers require diligence to maintain moisture levels in potting mixes. Check soil moisture frequently, water thoroughly when the top inch becomes dry, and empty excess water that collects in drain trays. Misting fronds often boost humidity around the plants. Move containers to sheltered areas during extreme heat, winds, or cold snaps. Indoor plants appreciate humidifiers and grouping with other houseplants to raise moisture levels. Keep potted ferns away from heating vents, radiators, and drafty areas.

Gardeners in USDA zones 8-10 can achieve dazzling permanent fern beds for year-round enjoyment. Hardy evergreen varieties like holly fern, autumn fern, and Japanese-painted fern thrive outdoors, with minimal frost protection needed. Prepare planting beds with rich organic soil, ample drainage, and mulch. Dress beds with hardscape features like pathways, benches, and stones complement the verdant ferns. Overwintering ferns dormant in a greenhouse or cool basement can still provide gorgeous greenery for gardeners in colder zones during the growing season.

With over 10,000 diverse fern species, gardeners have copious options to incorporate these striking plants. Their graceful nature, variety of forms and colors, and ease of care make ferns ideal additions to gardens and container plantings. The next time you visit a nursery or garden center, bring home some container ferns and allow these mesmerizing plants to weave their lush magic in your own garden.

Rare and Endangered Fern Species

Ferns dominated the plant world for over 200 million years, but today, many species face the threat of extinction. While ferns as a group are still widely dispersed, at least 1,000 species are classified as endangered or vulnerable by the International Union for Conservation of Nature (IUCN). Habitat loss, climate change, invasive species, and over-collection continue to endanger fragile fern populations worldwide. However, ongoing conservation efforts aim to protect these unique living fossils that have existed since before the age of dinosaurs.

Many rare ferns cling to existence in small isolated populations within specialized environments. The critically endangered MacGillivray's spleenwort of Australia grows only in humid cinder caves. The Santa Clara Valley Dudleya, California's rarest fern, occupies a single valley oak grove. Tiny Kinghorn's holly fern survives on a lone Hawaiian lava flow while the Koolau mountain cliff fern teeters on eroded cliffs of one Hawaiian mountain range. Since their habitats are so restricted, these species are extremely vulnerable. Any disruption could wipe them out completely.

Deforestation and habitat conversion for agriculture, development, and mining have destroyed or fragmented the habitats of many rare ferns. Due to residential construction, slender cliff brake, a Florida endangered species, has vanished from 60% of its original sites. Puerto Rico's crested quillwort occupies less than 20 wetland acres, threatened by infrastructure projects and pollution. The illegal removal of wild plants for the horticultural trade has also decimated some species. Over-collection of the popular Queen Sago palm fern reduced its population by 80% in just a few years.

Invasive species are another serious threat, displacing native ferns or outcompeting them for resources. The Australian climbing brake fern struggles to survive amidst invasions of exotic vines. Cuba's dwarf polypody and Haiti's giant filmy fern contend with African tulip tree overgrowth engulfing their rocky habitats. Even introduced herbivores endanger ferns. Feral goats nearly decimated the tough wild cinnamon fern endemic to certain Hawaiian islands.

Climate change also jeopardizes rare ferns with specific ecological requirements. Warming trends and reduced humidity affect cloud forest-dwelling Andean sword ferns. The Cumberland Island fern only exists on one Georgia island, and rising sea levels could inundate its limited range. Extreme weather events like tropical cyclones wipe out substantial populations in an instant. Hurricane Maria destroyed half the wild individuals of Costa Rica's ornate polypody fern in a single night.

Conservation measures focus on habitat protection, captive breeding, and public education to protect rare ferns. Critical habitats can be preserved through the establishment of nature reserves, national parks, and wilderness areas. These afford legal protections that restrict detrimental human activities. Captive propagation at botanical gardens and nurseries aims to establish ex-situ populations as security against extinction. Sensitive habitats can even be replicated at these facilities to foster successful reintroduction. Public outreach underscores the importance of biological conservation among local communities whose cooperation is critical for effective habitat protection.

While the situation seems dire for many endangered ferns, some positive strides give hope. Aggressive efforts have tripled populations of the Wilkes's holly fern in Hawaii. The rediscovery of certain endangered species, like the Khangchendzonga filmy fern, highlights how much we still have yet to learn. Researchers continue discovering previously unknown rare ferns, like a new moonwort species located in 2017 after lying unidentified in a herbarium for over 60 years. Our expanding botanical knowledge and passion for conservation could still save these priceless natural treasures that offer a living glimpse into the distant past.

Protecting the unique biodiversity of ferns is a challenging endeavor, but countless dedicated individuals and organizations devote themselves to this worthy cause. The International Union for the Conservation of Nature monitors endangered species and facilitates coordinated conservation action. Non-profits like the American Fern Society promote fern preservation through direct habitat management activities and funding research grants. Citizen scientists help locate populations, propagate species, and monitor habitats. Botanical institutions like the New York Botanical Garden and Chicago Botanic Garden maintain living collections of rare ferns for public education and reintroduction.

Home gardeners can also make a difference using best practices when cultivating ferns. Avoid purchasing ferns dug from the wild and be wary of unfamiliar species likely poached illegally. Select nursery-propagated ferns instead to reduce demand pressures on wild populations. Prevent naturalized exotic ferns from escaping cultivation and displacing native plants. Join local conservancies to volunteer to protect wilderness areas that harbor rare ferns. Support botanical institutions engaged in conservation work. Even cultivating endangered species at home helps raise public awareness of biodiversity issues.

Though often overlooked compared to showier flowering plants, ferns offer an irreplaceable connection to the primordial origins of plant life on Earth. Their tenacious persistence over hundreds of millions of years is inspirational. While threats to their survival are very real, ferns have survived ice ages, asteroid impacts, and massive climate shifts in the past. Through the efforts of impassioned scientists, conservationists, and everyday citizens, these antiquated wonders need not vanish in the modern age. With diligent protection of habitats and populations, our descendants centuries from now may still enjoy a diverse fern legacy - just as endless generations in the distant past once did.

The plight of endangered ferns illustrates how our collective actions threaten the intricate web of life that sustains our planet. But their story also underscores that human stewardship guided by wisdom and compassion can still preserve our imperiled natural heritage. Our species bears responsibility for protecting living relics like rare ferns, which recall that long expanse of ecological history that preceded human existence. Only by awakening ecological consciousness and promoting environmental ethics globally can we find a balanced path where humans and the wild can continue the ageless evolutionary journeys that produced such botanical marvels as ferns.

Chapter 3
Conifers and Gymnosperms

The Rise and Success of Gymnosperms

While ferns dominated the ancient world, another diverse group of seed plants was on the rise. The gymnosperms, meaning "naked seeds," exploded in abundance and variety during the Mesozoic era when dinosaurs still roamed. These advanced plants conquered drier habitats and grew taller than low-lying ferns. Conifers became the predominant gymnosperms, shaping extensive prehistoric forests. Although later overshadowed by more modern angiosperms, conifers and other gymnosperms remain integral components of global ecosystems today.

When gymnosperms first emerged over 300 million years ago, they held a tremendous evolutionary advantage over more primitive plants – seeds. Unlike spores dispersed by chance, seeds contain internal food reserves to nourish young sporophyte plants. This promoted survival and dispersion into new habitats. Gymnosperm pollen microspores were also delivered more directly to ovules than fern motile sperm, making fertilization more reliable. Seeds enabled gymnosperms to colonize drier upland areas, while lower groups like ferns still required moist environments.

The most successful early gymnosperms were the cordaites, now-extinct tree-like plants named for their strap-shaped leaves. They flourished during the Carboniferous and Permian periods but declined by the Triassic. Later, conifers became the predominant gymnosperm trees. Pinophyta, the conifer division, contains six families and over 600 species of cone-bearing trees and shrubs. Cones provided better protection for developing seeds than exposed structures like fern sporangia. In harsh or arid environments, this gave conifers the evolutionary edge they needed to survive.

Cycadophyta is another ancient gymnosperm division dating back to the Permian. It contains the cycads, an unusual tropical and subtropical palm-like tree group. They have changed little from their earliest forms but are now endangered relics. Ginkgophyta consists solely of the distinctive ginkgo, the sole survivor of a once diverse lineage. Gnetophyta contains three unusual genera of woody vines and shrubs limited to certain tropical regions. While conifers overwhelmingly dominate modern gymnosperm populations, these other persistent ancient lineages showcase gymnosperm diversity.

During the Mesozoic era, gymnosperms underwent major radiation and occupied most forest niches. Coniferous forests of ginkgos, sequoias, pine, and spruce ancestors blanketed higher latitudes. Strange monkey puzzle trees and araucaria conifers grew in now-extinct southern polar forests. Cycads, cypress trees, and palm-like bennettitales populated tropical lowlands. Overall, conifers adapted readily to specialized environments and proved extremely successful despite some setbacks.

The Cretaceous period saw substantial turnover in gymnosperm forests. Changing climates favored faster-growing flowering plants, which came to dominate lower-latitude forests. An asteroid impact 66 million years ago and massive volcanic eruptions dealt a catastrophic blow to gymnosperms and other species. However, tenacious conifers clung on in upland habitats and more northern latitudes. Given time to recover, they repopulated forests but now shared dominance with angiosperms.

Today, conifers thrive across northern regions, alpine areas, and arid habitats ill-suited to most flowering plants. The longevity and resilience of pines, firs, redwoods, junipers, and other conifers attest to the evolutionary advantages conferred by their primitive but effective seed-bearing adaptations. While perhaps lacking the colorful allure of ornate flowers, these living fossils provide ecological biodiversity and human utility over 300 million years after their gymnosperm ancestors first emerged and spread across primordial landscapes. The structure of gymnosperms also confers adaptive benefits. Their woody tissues allow taller growth forms than herbaceous plants, permitting competition for sunlight. Tall mature heights provide greater seed dispersal and expand habitat ranges. Some gymnosperm adaptations help reduce water loss, an advantage in drier areas. Thick bark insulates against fire, enabling survival in fire-prone ecosystems. Costly defenses like resin discourage herbivory. While perhaps not as showy as flowering plants, gymnosperms possess elegant, functional designs finely tuned by natural selection.

Genomic studies reveal gymnosperms have relatively large genomes compared to angiosperms. However, gene duplication is less common, so their genomes are simpler in some respects. Long lifespans and slow maturation periods characterize most gymnosperms. Some bristlecone pines exceed 4,000 years old. Cycads live over 1,000 years. Ginkgo trees can survive centuries while intricately adapted; gymnosperms lack some angiosperm innovations. They cannot produce diverse, colorful flowers to attract specialized pollinators. Most rely solely on wind for pollination. Only certain cycads use insect pollination. Their naked seeds also afford less protection for offspring than enclosed angiosperm seeds. However, tough seed coats and large energy reserves help compensate. Though they may seem primitive by comparison, gymnosperms exhibit exquisite evolutionary refinements reflecting hundreds of millions of years of natural selection.

Today, conifers continue to provide critical biodiversity, ecosystem services, and resources that support life. The taiga, spanning subarctic regions of Eurasia and North America, represents the largest land biome on Earth. Conifers like spruce, pine, and larch dominate these vast northern forests. They prevent soil erosion, regulate water cycles, and provide wildlife habitat. Logging these renewable conifer forests supplies timber, fuel, and pulpwood. Pine nuts and juniper berries offer edible crops. Conifer resins produce turpentine, varnishes, and perfumes. Their ecological and economic contributions remain incalculable.

While perhaps lacking the splashy appeal of flowers, gymnosperms offer quiet testimony to the power of natural evolutionary forces. Persisting for eons with gradual refinements, they became masters of their respective domains. When properly appreciated, their endurance, simplicity of form, and perfection of function reflect nature's profound wisdom. Our human efforts will struggle to improve on what these primeval plants have already achieved through countless small adjustments accumulated over the course of time.

Conifer Diversity and Identification

While sharing basic similarities, the conifers exhibit impressive diversity in their forms, adaptations, and natural ranges. Over 600 species exist worldwide, inhabiting all continents except Antarctica. Identifying characteristics helps distinguish the major groups. This aids in appreciating their variability and relationships. Understanding conifer diversity provides insight into their long evolutionary history and ecological importance.

All conifers bear cones and needle or scale-like evergreen leaves. However, these features' size, shape, and arrangement help differentiate the major families. Pines typically have slender, clustered needles and oval woody cones. Firs display short, flat, singular needles and erect cylindrical cones. Cypresses and junipers have small, scale-like leaves and round, berry-like cones. Larches produce tufts of soft needles that turn golden and shed in autumn.

Spruces exhibit short, square, 4-angled needles. Their drooping cones have thin, overlapping scales that peel back at maturity. Hemlocks possess delicate, flat sprays of short needles and tiny cones on short stalks. Podocarp pines share characteristics of both pines and yews, with elliptical flattened needles. Kauri pines produce leathery leaves, often with frosted white undersides and large spherical cones. These variations aid identification and reflect ecological adaptations.

Conifer sizes range from prostrate ground covers to towering 200-foot giants. Dwarf Siberian pine hugs alpine slopes while towering coast redwoods reach skyward—scale-like junipers sprawl as groundcovers. Stately, Douglas firs dominated northwest forests. Cushion-forming pines survive brutal subarctic exposures. Sizes align with environmental conditions, conferring advantages. Cones and crown shapes also vary between open, closed, pendulous, or upright forms. Subtle differences offer identification clues.

Geographic distributions provide more identification markers and highlight conifer adaptability. Pines populate warmer climates. Lodgepole pines define western mountain forests, while white pines grace eastern woods. Firs prefer northern latitudes and high altitudes. Norway spruce inhabits European forests. Unique island pine species evolved in isolation. Boreal larches range across northern Canada and Eurasia. Junipers withstand arid and semi-arid areas—specific ranges developed over eons of gradual migration, diversification, and extinction.

Conifer habitats include boreal and mountain forests, swampy wetlands, sandy soils, acidic bogs, and alpine regions. Hardy pines and firs dominate northern forests, while cypresses occupy southern swamps. Lodgepole pines favor fire ecology. Coastal redwoods need Pacific fog. Bristlecones endure harsh conditions on rocky summits. Habitat preferences reflect specialized adaptations to soils, precipitation, temperatures, light levels, and other environmental factors. Even shade tolerance varies.

While sharing basic attributes, conifer diversity allows identification and reveals their long evolutionary journey. Subtle variations equip them for widespread habitats and changing conditions over time. Differing leaf shapes and sizes regulate temperature and moisture. Contrasting crown forms maximize light exposure. Their richness provides ecological health and inspires human appreciation. Conifer diversity represents nature's endless capacity for invention through small progressive modifications accumulated over countless generations. Conifer chemistry provides further identification clues. Unique scents come from compounds like terpenes, lending distinctive aromas when leaves or cones are crushed. Spruces and firs smell pleasantly of citrus and pine. Coast redwoods exude a spicy scent. Desert cypress junipers emit a woody, resinous odor. Waxy or powdery coatings on needles and cones also aid recognition. The white powder on blue spruce needles rubs off.

Most conifers display amazing adaptations to specific environments. Diversity equips them to inhabit diverse regions and conditions. Variations in size, form, foliage, cones, and growth habits allow identification while reflecting evolutionary refinements. Appreciating conifer diversity accentuates their excellence as hardy survivors.

However, many rare and endemic conifers face extinction dangers. Seventy-five conifer species rank critically endangered, endangered, or vulnerable. Habitat loss, climate change, invasive species, disease, and human exploitation threaten fragile populations. Conservation efforts strive to protect gene pool diversity and prevent permanent loss. Preserving conifer biodiversity preserves irreplaceable natural heritage.

Home gardeners can cultivate scaled-down versions of conifer diversity. Miniature cultivars of many species adapt well to backyard growing. Dwarf Alberta spruce and dwarf Hinoki cypress make excellent compact specimens for garden beds or containers. Prostrate shore juniper and rock cotoneaster form low evergreen groundcovers. Unique pendulous forms like weeping Alaska cedar gracefully cascade where space allows. For smaller spaces, bonsai pines, larches, and hemlocks display the charm of their larger counterparts.

Growing an assortment of dwarf conifers makes an attractively varied display. Combine finely needled forms with varieties having scale-like foliage. Contrast columnar shapes with mounding or prostrate habits. Showcase interesting hues like blue spruce, golden arborvitae, or variegated Japanese false cypress. Let dainty lacebark pines mingle with sturdy dwarf mugo pines. Creating a miniature conifer collection captures nature's abundance in smaller spaces.

Conifer diversity represents eons of evolutionary expression, ecological richness, and natural beauty.

Conifer Ecology and Habitats

Conifers populate diverse ecosystems across the globe thanks to specialized adaptations that equip them to thrive in specific habitats. Understanding relationships between conifer ecology and associated environments provides insight into their evolutionary resilience. Different conifer species dominate boreal forests, temperate woodlands, tropical cloud forests, coastal swamps, and alpine zones based on the environmental conditions each group can best tolerate.

Boreal forests blanketing subarctic regions showcase conifer hardiness. Spruce, fir, pine, larch, and other cold-resistant species comprise the vast northern taiga, representing Earth's largest land biome. Hardy conifers withstand brutally cold winters and short growing seasons where few other plants persist. Their global distribution and adaptations help regulate northern ecosystems.

Various conifers also populate temperate forests farther south. Pines, firs, hemlocks, redwoods, cypresses, and others mix with deciduous angiosperm trees like oaks, maples, and birches. Fall deciduous leaf drop reduces competition for sunlight during winter when conifers maintain photosynthetic activity. Coniferous forests around the world showcase geographic speciation reflecting regional conditions.

Surprising diversity occurs in tropical and subtropical cloud forests typically dominated by broadleaf evergreen trees. However, tropical conifers like araucarias, podocarps, and some cypress relatives occupy wet high-elevation niches. Dense fog provides constant moisture to complement abundant rainfall. Cooler temperatures allow gymnosperms to share tropical forest canopies with angiosperm trees.

Coastal swamps and wetlands present challenges overcome by specialized conifers. Bald cypress and pond cypress thrive in southern U.S. floodplains. Dawn redwoods inhabit marshes and wetlands in China. Mangrove pines and pitch pines grow along sandy coastal areas. Adaptations like aerial roots, salt tolerance, and flexible needles allow coastal conifers to occupy unique ecological niches.

Hardy conifers also extend into alpine areas, seemingly prohibitive for trees. Bristlecone pines, foxtail pines, and dwarf Siberian pines survive brutal wind, intense sun, poor soil, and extremes of heat and cold in high mountain habitats. Hardy conifers expand tree vegetation into otherwise treeless alpine zones—their capacity to thrive where other species cannot highlight their rugged adaptive abilities.

Conifer ecology intimately connects with associated forest habitats. Over evolutionary timeframes, speciation and adaptation resulted in certain groups dominating specific environments. Understanding relationships between conifers and their native habitats provides essential ecological form and function insights. Exploring those connections continues to reveal nature's ingenious methods for propagating and protecting plant life across our planet in myriad climates and conditions. Conifers play many vital ecological roles in their native habitats. Their extensive root systems control erosion while absorbing runoff and preventing floods. Needle canopies regulate regional rainfall. Conifer forests purify air, absorb carbon, and moderate climates. Cavities in mature trees provide nesting sites. Dropped needles and cones enrich soil as they decompose. Conifer habitats support diverse animal, insect, and plant life.

Some conifers exhibit strong symbiotic relationships with fungi. Mycorrhizal fungi colonize conifer roots, helping absorb nutrients and water in exchange for sugars. Fungal sheaths protect tender feeder roots. Some fungi even connect multiple trees, allowing networked distribution of resources to weaker individuals. Conifers, in turn, provide fungi with nutrients and habitats.

Conifers also cope with environmental hazards common to their native regions. Adaptations like fire-resistant bark and serotiny help pines regenerate after periodic wildfires. Flexible needles and asymmetric crown shapes minimize snow and ice damage in northern climes. Silviculture techniques model natural dynamics to manage productive timber forests. Understanding ecological relationships helps maximize environmental and economic benefits.

However, climate change now threatens the future of many conifer habitats. Warming trends push conifers poleward or to higher elevations outside current ranges. Drier conditions stress trees and increase fire, insect, and disease outbreaks. Intense storms and erratic weather patterns endanger forests. Fragmentation limits migration opportunities. To ensure ecosystem continuity, creating migration corridors through habitat connectivity could aid displacement. Assisted population transfer to more suitable locations is also being investigated.

Home gardeners can support conifer ecology through proper landscape planting. Selecting suitable species adapted to local conditions is fundamental. Providing appropriate moisture, light, soil, and space reduces stress. Discouraging exotic pests and pathogens protects forest health. Allowing natural duff accumulation mimics forest nutrient cycling. Conifers planted in urban areas confer ecological benefits well beyond gardens.

The intimate bonds between conifers and their native habitats showcase an interconnected natural world. As ancient living links to primordial forests, conifers exemplify sturdy sylvan resilience through dynamic environmental changes over eons. But modern human impacts now threaten the continuity and health of many conifer ecosystems. Understanding their ecological relationships better equips us to protect these iconic forests and the web of life intertwined with enduring conifers.

Uses of Conifers in Forestry and Horticulture

Conifers, also known as cone-bearing trees, have been invaluable resources for human civilization for thousands of years. With over 600 species spread across the globe, conifers are extensively used for timber, paper, resin, and ornamental purposes. Understanding the properties and uses of different conifers has allowed us to sustainably utilize these trees and cultivate them in forestry plantations and gardens.

The softwood timber derived from conifers has been a staple construction material throughout history. Trees such as pine, fir, spruce, and cedar provide strong, lightweight lumber that is relatively easy to work with. Softwoods are less dense than hardwoods, allowing them to be harvested younger and replenished more rapidly in tree plantations. Conifer wood has been utilized to build everything from homes and ships to furniture and tools. Even today, well over half of lumber production globally comes from conifers.

Beyond lumber, conifers have also been important sources of pulp and paper. For paper production, fast-growing conifers like pine and spruce can be harvested in as little as 15 years. The cellulose fiber extracted from conifer wood gives paper its strength and durability. Important paper products derived from conifers include newspapers, paper bags, cardboard, tissues, and more. Conifers play an integral role in developing paper industries.

In addition to wood, conifers have supplied other important products. Pine resin and tar have had many uses, from sealing ships to waterproofing ropes. Spruce gum was chewed as an early form of chewing gum. Some conifer barks have been used for insulation, roofing, and canoe construction. Even conifer needles have utility, having been used as packing material, livestock bedding, and thatching. With so many parts of the tree proving useful, it's no wonder conifers have been so heavily utilized.

Beyond industrial applications, conifers have also been extremely popular horticulturally. Many conifers have compact growth habits, interesting textures, and year-round color, making them versatile landscape plants. Popular garden and ornamental conifers include dwarf spruces, junipers, false cypresses, and pines. Slow-growing conifers are often trained into the spectacular living sculptures found in Japanese gardens. Conifers also make classic Christmas trees and are often cut or dug up to bring their festive greenery indoors for the holidays.

Several factors have made conifers particularly desirable in the horticulture trade. Many tolerate pruning well, making them adaptable to hedges and topiary. Their evergreen nature provides year-round interest without dropping messy leaves. Conifers grow well in poor soil conditions, which would cause other plants to struggle. Many also have relatively few insect and disease problems. For homeowners and landscapers alike, conifers can serve as attractive, low-maintenance additions to gardens and landscapes.

Conifers will undoubtedly continue to play important roles, both environmentally and economically. Sustainable forestry practices can ensure conifers keep supplying wood products while also maintaining healthy forests. Conifer plantations sequester immense amounts of carbon when managed properly. Meanwhile, horticultural interest in new conifer cultivars shows no signs of waning. With a greater understanding of these diverse and versatile trees, we can continue benefiting from conifers' resources while ensuring their conservation. Whether building a house, publishing a book, or beautifying a garden, conifers will remain indispensable. While conifers clearly have tremendous utility, they also face substantial threats such as logging, land clearing, invasive pests, and climate change. However, with sustainable practices and active management, we can ensure the perpetuation of these valuable trees.

One of the biggest dangers to conifers is unsustainable logging. While properly regulated forestry aims for responsible harvests and regrowth, illegal logging completely disregards conservation. Entire old-growth forests of massive conifers have been decimated for quick profits. Even selective legal logging removes the largest, most robust trees, leaving forests full of smaller, younger trees. This can diminish the biodiversity and ecosystem functions of conifer forests over time. Implementing stronger protections for ancient, intact forests could help conserve these diminishing habitats.

Along with logging, land clearing for agriculture or development poses risks. As human populations grow, there is increasing pressure to convert forested areas to other uses. This directly eliminates conifer habitat while also fragmenting the remaining forest blocks. Fragmentation makes forests more vulnerable to drying out and invasive species. Setting aside larger reserves and corridors between them can help maintain connectivity for conifer forests. Promoting cluster development rather than sprawl also limits encroachment.

Invasive insects and diseases have taken a major toll on some conifers. Non-native pests like emerald ash borer, woolly adelgid, and Dutch elm disease have decimated ash, hemlock, and elm tree populations. Once introduced, these pests spread rampantly due to a lack of natural controls. Quarantines, pesticides, and biological control agents have had limited success combating them. Diversifying landscapes with many conifer species can limit susceptibility to any pest outbreak. Breeding-resistant cultivars may also strengthen conifers against exotic invaders.

Climate change presents complex risks to conifers worldwide. Rising temperatures allow insects and diseases to expand ranges and increase reproduction. Meanwhile, droughts impair conifers already living near their drought tolerance limits. Models suggest substantial future declines in conifer habitats globally. Assisted migration efforts may be needed to help valued conifers transition to more suitable climates. Meanwhile, reducing other stressors can help make forests more resilient to shifting conditions.

Protecting remaining old-growth stands is crucial for preserving conifer biodiversity. These ancient forests house many rare species uniquely adapted to those habitats. In western North America, old-growth conifer ecosystems have declined to just a tiny fraction of their former extent. Creating new reserves on public lands could safeguard some of these increasingly rare forests. Similar ancient pine, spruce, and fir forests in Russia, Scandinavia, and beyond require protection as well.

At the species level, many conifers face grave threats. Several firs and spruces are endangered, with just a handful of surviving trees. Their limited numbers and restricted ranges leave them highly vulnerable to extinction. Habitat restoration, legal protection, propagation, and reintroduction offer hope for their recovery. Other conifers, like giant sequoia, face longer-term climate change perils. Keeping sizable, functional ecosystems intact will be key to preserving sequoia groves over the coming centuries.

Though challenges are formidable, the future need not be bleak for Earth's conifers. With ecological foresight and responsible practices, we can sustain our utilization of conifer resources while also conserving their biodiversity and ecosystem services. This symbiotic relationship has served humanity well over the past millennia and can continue doing so indefinitely. However, it will require increased environmental awareness and action to protect these invaluable trees for generations to come.

Unusual Conifers from Around the World

Conifers exist everywhere except Antarctica. Their resilient roots allow them to thrive everywhere, from rainforests to tundras. While pines, firs, spruces, and cedars may be the most familiar conifers, there are many lesser-known and unusual conifer species around the world. These unique conifers have adapted to thrive in environments that other trees find inhospitable. Studying these unusual conifers provides insight into the resilience and flexibility of conifer evolution.

One of the most bizarre and ancient conifers is the monkey puzzle tree, with the scientific name Araucaria araucana. As its common name suggests, the intricate branching patterns and overlapping razor-sharp leaves make it difficult to climb. Monkey puzzle trees come from the Andes Mountains in South America, growing at 3,000-4,500 feet. The trees can live for up to 1,300 years—their unusual appearance results from evolutionary adaptations to dry conditions and volcanic soils. The overlapping scale-like leaves provide excellent insulation to conserve water. Fossil evidence shows Araucaria trees were once widespread during the Jurassic period millions of years ago when dinosaurs roamed the earth. Today, monkey puzzle trees are endangered in their native range, although they remain popular ornamental trees in parks and gardens around the world.

The Wollemi pine is another "living fossil" conifer dating back to the age of dinosaurs. With the scientific name Wollemia nobilis, this critically endangered species was discovered in Australia in 1994 in a remote canyon. Previous fossils indicated the Wollemi pine was extinct for millions of years, yet an isolated population survived undetected. These majestic pines can grow 130 feet tall and trunk diameters over three feet across. Their bark is bubbly with deep grooves. Wollemi pines have thin, narrow leaves arranged in rows that help regulate water loss in dry environments. Less than 100 mature trees exist in the wild, but the Wollemi pine remains a source of hope that other relic species are still undiscovered. The Bristlecone pine holds the record as the oldest known individual tree at over 5,000 years old. These gnarly pines are highly adapted to the harsh conditions of high mountains in Nevada, California, and Utah. Bristlecones have deep taproots to find water and mottled bark with resin ducts that protect from insects and fungal infections. Their stunted growth form and strip-like needles minimize water loss and damage from fierce winds. Under ideal conditions, bristlecones can live over 5,000 years, earning them the nickname "methuselah trees." Their longevity provides a valuable record of climate conditions over millennia.

The dragon's blood tree, Dracaena cinnabari, is a prehistoric conifer on just a few Indian Ocean islands. With bizarre umbrella-shaped crowns perched atop spindly trunks, these trees resemble creatures from mythology. Dragon's blood trees take decades to mature and may live for 650 years. Their name comes from the trees' red sap, which ancient cultures used for medicine and dyes. These slow-growing trees require very specific habitat conditions, which restrict them to granite mountainsides with moisture from coastal fog. Only around 600 mature dragon's blood trees are left in the wild. Ongoing conservation efforts aim to protect them from extinction.

The strangest conifer on earth may be the Welwitschia mirabilis, found only in the Namib Desert in southern Africa. Unlike any other plant, welwitschias have just two strap-shaped leaves that grow continuously from the base throughout the plant's lifetime, reaching over 13 feet long. With male and female cones, welwitschias reproduce by wind-borne pollination. Individual plants can live over 1,500 years in hyperarid desert conditions. Their anomalous form is another relic of bygone eras. Unfortunately, welwitschias suffer degraded habitats from mining and climate change. They are listed as vulnerable, with major efforts underway to establish protected areas.

Conifers continue to fascinate botanists and gardeners with their structural and evolutionary diversity. Studying rare habitat specialists like the bristlecones, dragon's blood trees, and welwitschias provides a window into conifer adaptations over eons. While human activities threaten many unusual conifer species, efforts to preserve genetic diversity aim to ensure their survival. Unusual conifers persist as living museums displaying the endless creativity of natural selection across millennia. They deserve protected sanctuaries so future generations can experience their majesty.

Threats Facing Conifers Globally

Conifers have thrived for over 300 million years and continue to be ecologically and economically important across the globe. However, many conifer species face existential threats from human activities and climate change. Awareness of the various perils facing conifers is key for conservation efforts. This section examines the major hazards jeopardizing conifer survival worldwide.

Habitat loss poses the most immediate threat to many conifers. Deforestation for timber, agriculture, and development destroys the ecosystems where conifers have evolved over millennia. Old-growth forests with towering ancient conifers cannot be easily replaced. Even when forests regenerate, the new landscape may not suit native conifer populations that rely on mutualisms lost in the process. Fragmentation also reduces habitat connectivity needed for gene flow and species migrations. For example, the endangered Pinus maximartinezii in Mexico has lost over 98% of individuals due to illegal logging of its cloud forest habitat. Protecting intact habitats and biological corridors is essential.

Invasive pests and diseases transported through global trade have devastated certain conifers. Well-known examples include chestnut blight, Dutch elm disease, and hemlock woolly adelgid. White pine blister rust similarly damages valuable five-needle pines across North America. Invasive insects like the emerald ash borer and red turpentine beetle have also led to mass conifer deaths. Warmer winters enable the greater spread of these attackers. Using integrated pest management and genetic research can help protect conifers from exotic, harmful organisms.

Conifers adapted to rare or extreme environments are especially climate-sensitive. Higher temperatures and shifting precipitation patterns can make their restricted habitats uninhabitable. Alpine species like bristlecone pine are migrating poleward and upward in elevation but may eventually run out of room on the mountains. Coastal redwoods and mangroves suffer declines from sea level rise, saltwater intrusion, and storms. Assisted migration, adaptive breeding, and ex-situ conservation provide hope for some climate-challenged conifer species. However, projections indicate certain relic conifer populations are likely to go extinct in their native ranges. Pollution also threatens conifers and their ecosystems. Acid rain damages conifer needles and depletes soils of nutrients. Ozone pollution likewise impairs conifer growth and defenses against insects and disease. Excess nitrogen and sulfur emissions favor invasive species over native conifers with lower nutrient preferences. Mining, oil drilling, and fracking introduce contaminants that can kill conifers through direct toxicity or altering soil chemistry. Even recreational activities like off-road vehicles can severely degrade fragile conifer habitats such as desert soil crusts. Enforcing clean air and water regulations protects conifers and entire forest communities.

Unsustainable forestry practices, including overharvesting, short rotations, and poor regeneration, further endanger conifer forests. Maximizing immediate yields decimates the most commercially valuable large trees, leaving few mother trees to reseed for the next generation. Most timber is also harvested from natural forests despite lower productivity and biodiversity than selectively bred, intensively managed plantations. Implementing low-impact forestry systems tailored to regional ecology could maintain productive timber yields while conserving natural forests.

The complex interactions highlighting the plight of conifers in a human-dominated world necessitate holistic conservation solutions. Integrating conifer habitats into protected area networks helps maintain ecosystem integrity against multiple threats. Assisted migration and ex-situ propagation preserve conifer gene pools for future restoration. Strategic use of emerging technologies like gene editing may enhance conifer resilience to rapid environmental change. Ultimately, addressing unsustainable consumption and policies valuing immediate profits over ecological sustainability is required to ensure the perpetuity of global conifer forests. Proactively mitigating climate change, reducing pollution, restoring habitats, and adopting sustainable practices can safeguard the magnificent conifers that have shaped environments for eons.

Chapter 4

Flowering Plants: Monocots

What Makes a Monocot?

Monocots are one of the major groups of flowering plants, distinguished from eudicots by their differing anatomical characteristics. While monocots and eudicots dominate most terrestrial habitats today, they evolved from a common ancestor around 140-150 million years ago during the Early Cretaceous period.

The most recognizable feature of monocots is in their name - having one embryonic seed leaf or cotyledon. When monocot seeds germinate, a single cotyledon emerges from the seed coat. This contrasts with two seed leaves typically seen in eudicots. However, some monocots may exhibit two cotyledons under certain conditions, making this trait unreliable for identification on its own.

Instead, examining the vascular system provides definitive evidence for monocot classification. Monocot stems contain scattered vascular bundles, with xylem and phloem distributed irregularly through the fibrous matrix. Meanwhile, eudicots have concentric rings of xylem and phloem in their woody stems. Roots also show differences, with monocots having a central core of vascular tissue compared to a ring in most eudicots.

Monocot leaf veins display parallel venation where bundles run straight and parallel from the base to the tip of the leaf blade. Eudicots, on the other hand, have branching reticulate venation with smaller veins interconnecting in net-like patterns. Grasses perfectly exemplify the monocot venation concept.

Monocot flowers also exhibit distinctive anatomy, often with flower parts arranged in threes or multiples of three instead of the eudicot pattern of fours and fives. Reproductive organs tend to be trimerous as well. The pollen grains produced by monocots are characteristically boat-shaped with a single indentation or pore, contrasting with eudicot pollen, which usually contains three apertures and pores. Other shared traits help define monocots as well. Their root systems tend to be more diffuse and fibrous compared to taproots in many eudicots. Reproductive morphology also shows tendencies - monocots frequently have similar inconspicuous petals and sepals, while eudicots usually have distinct, showy flower parts.

Monocot leaves are longer and thinner with unbranched veins, contrasting with shorter, broader eudicot leaves and branching venation. However, there are exceptions where some monocots develop wider leaves, and eudicots have slender linear leaves. Thus, leaf morphology alone does not reliably indicate monocot identity.

In terms of growth form, monocots favor linear, unbranched stems and strap or needle-like leaves. Many grow from underground bulbs or tubers. Eudicots exhibit greater variation in growth habits, including branching woody stems and broad leaves. But again, exceptions exist, such as branched monocot bamboo and tree-like palms.

While the common diagnostic traits help distinguish monocots from other angiosperms, diversity within the monocots reveals the flexibility of their adaptations. Not all monocots express every characteristic. Still, the tendencies reflect underlying genetic and developmental patterns shared among monocot lineages since their evolutionary divergence from other flowering plants.

Molecular evidence provides additional insights into monocot identity. Genetic analyses show monocots share a common ancestor and form a monophyletic group - meaning the living monocots contain all descendants of their progenitor lineage. Specific gene mutations shared by monocots but not eudicots indicate evolutionary similarities.

Synthesizing the anatomical, morphological, and genetic evidence creates a robust picture of how monocots are uniquely developed to thrive in diverse environments. Their distinguishing features reflect common developmental constraints and evolutionary adaptations. While variations occur within monocot orders, the unifying traits bind them as an identifiable, ecologically important segment of the plant kingdom. Understanding what makes a monocot provides a foundation for appreciating their biological diversity and evolutionary history.

Grasses, Sedges, and Rushes

The monocot order Poales contains diverse families of grasses, sedges, and rushes, which dominate many ecosystems as primary plant life. From lawn turf to staple cereal crops, grasses impact human economies and cultures worldwide. Sedges and rushes often thrive in wet, marginal environments. This section examines key traits and distributions of the grass, sedge, and rush botanical families.

With over 10,000 species, the grass family Poaceae provides staple foods that nourish humankind. Maize, rice, wheat, barley, oats, rye, millets, sugar cane, and sorghum are derived from cultivated grasses. Bamboos, a grass subfamily, also has over 1,000 species used for building materials, food, and ornamentals. Beyond crops, grasses provide livestock forage and form foundational habitats like prairies, savannas, and steppes. Identifying features of grasses include hollow stems with collar-like nodes, two-ranked leaves, fusoid cells for water storage, and spikelet flowers.

Sedges differ from grasses by having solid, triangular stems and leaves arranged in three ranks. The sedge family Cyperaceae dominates wetlands globally, with over 5,500 species. Many sedges have superficially grass-like leaves, especially the dominant genus Carex, with over 2,000 species. Sedges thrive in marshes, swamps, fens, riparian zones, and damp forests. The sedge, known as papyrus, Cyperus papyrus, provided ancient writing material. Sedges produce nut-like fruits called achenes. They provide food sources, habitat, stream bank stabilization, and wetland filtration functions.

The rush family Juncaceae contains around 300 species of rushes worldwide. Often inhabiting bogs, marshes, pond margins, and streamsides rushes frequent wet soils. Rushes have stiff, round stems with internal piths. Their small flowers have scaly bracts and tepals in two fused whorls. Leaves are reduced to basal sheaths in many species, adding to the spiky appearance of rushes. Various rushes were used for basket weaving, mats, chairs, and ornamentals. The genus Juncus dominates and is tolerant of saline and alkali conditions. Desert rushes uniquely form a large part of microbiotic soil crusts. While superficially grass-like, rushes fill wet niche habitats within monocot plant communities. The shared characteristics of grasses, sedges, and rushes reflect their membership in the monocot order Poales. However, their adaptations allow the partitioning of terrestrial and wetland environments. Grasses dominate drier areas, with flashy flowers attracting wind and insect pollination. Sedges prevail in saturated soils, aided by unisexual tiny flowers relying on wind pollination. Rushes compete for marginal wet habitats, their inconspicuous flowers spreading by passive self-pollination.

Together, these three monocot families form the foundation of many ecosystems. Grasslands sequester carbon, filter water, and prevent erosion. Wetland sedges and rushes mitigate flooding, absorb excess nutrients, and provide wildlife habitat. At a global scale, Poales derivatives, including rice, wheat, maize, millet, and bamboo, comprise the main food sources for our species. Beyond provisions, grasses, sedges, and rushes furnish materials for construction, clothing, basketry, ornamentals, and more.

However, the Poales families face threats from human activity. Agricultural irrigation drains wetlands, reducing sedge and rush extent. Livestock overgrazing degrades native grasslands. Pollution and invasive species also disrupt Poale's habitats. Climate change poses challenges through shifting precipitation patterns and extreme weather. Meanwhile, only a tiny fraction of Poales diversity gets preserved in ex-situ germplasm collections.

Concerted efforts are needed to catalog Poale species diversity and protect their genetic heritage. Sustainable agroecosystems can maintain productive grass crops while mimicking native grassland communities. Wetland restorations provide habitat recovery for sedges and rushes. Integrative in-situ and ex-situ approaches are necessary to safeguard the Poales families that sustain global ecosystems and human civilizations.

Orchids and Bromeliads

The monocot order Asparagales contains diverse ornate families, Orchidaceae and Bromeliaceae, prized for their exotic flowers and adaptive forms. Orchids comprise the largest family of flowering plants, with over 28,000 species. Bromeliads contain over 3,000 species, dominating tropical canopy habitats. This section explores the remarkable diversity and adaptations of orchids and bromeliads.

As a family, orchids display an astonishing array of floral shapes, colors, and pollination strategies. Petal modifications create landing platforms, nectar guides, or pseudo-sexual organs to attract specific pollinators. Some orchids mimic female insects via pheromones to seduce male insect pollinators. Orchids inhabit diverse ecosystems, from rainforests to deserts. Epiphytic orchids form a major component of tropical forest canopies. Terrestrial orchids abound in temperate grasslands and woods.

Orchids achieve ecological success through intimate relationships with fungal symbionts that enhance seed germination and provide nutrients. Their tiny, dust-like seeds embed fungal partners for germination. Orchid protocorms later obtain carbon from associated mycorrhizal fungi. Some orchids remain dependent on their fungal symbionts throughout life. This mycoheterotrophy allows orchids to colonize marginal habitats.

Orchids achieve ecological success through intimate relationships with fungal symbionts that enhance seed germination and provide nutrients. Their tiny, dust-like seeds embed fungal partners for germination. Orchid protocorms later obtain carbon from associated mycorrhizal fungi. Some orchids remain dependent on their fungal symbionts throughout life. This mycoheterotrophy allows orchids to colonize marginal habitats.

The bromeliad family also forms key pieces of Neotropical ecosystems. Bromeliads trap water and debris in their central tanks or axils with rosettes of waxy, strap-shaped leaves. These impoundments support complex food webs with frogs, insects, and other fauna. Bromeliads derive nutrients from trapped organic matter. Their tightly packed leaf scales minimize water loss. Trichomes absorb moisture from humid air. These adaptations allow bromeliads to thrive in tropical forest canopies. The majority of bromeliad species are epiphytic, thriving in humid tropical forests. However, about a quarter of bromeliad species grow on rocks, beach dunes, or soil. These demonstrate the flexible adaptations of bromeliads to dry environments. For example, the succulent terrestrial bromeliad Deuterocohnia has water-storing leaves adapted to arid conditions.

Beyond ecologic services, orchids and bromeliads provide human value. Orchids are prized for horticulture, supplying the multi-billion dollar cut flower and houseplant industries. Vanilla flavoring derives from cured orchid pods. Bromeliads, like the edible pineapple and fibrous sisal, also produce food, fiber, and ornamentals.

However, many rare orchids and bromeliads risk going extinct. Orchid habitats suffer from deforestation and illegal collection from the wild. The epiphytic lifecycle of orchids and bromeliads makes them vulnerable when host trees get logged. Climate change threatens cloud forest ecosystems where many orchids and bromeliads occur—expanding agriculture and development compounds habitat degradation.

Conservation of orchids and bromeliads will require integrated efforts. Habitat protection maintains native pollinator networks and fungi that sustain orchids. Seed banking and artificial propagation can supplement wild populations. Sustainable harvesting and orchard cultivation provide income while alleviating poaching pressures. Showcasing the remarkable biodiversity of orchids and bromeliads inspires public engagement in conserving these iconic monocot families.

Palms, Bananas, and Gingers

Several other important monocot families fall within the order Zingiberales, including palms, bananas, and gingers. Palms form a signature component of tropical landscapes, playing ecological roles from mangroves to desert oases. Bananas and plantains provide invaluable carbohydrates to our diets. Gingers add spice and ornamental diversity. This section explores the distinct biology of palms, bananas, and gingers.

With over 2,600 species, palms display an array of forms adapted to diverse environments. Most palms are distinguished by their large pinnate or palmate leaves, lack of secondary growth, and large clustered fruits. Palms inhabit rainforests, swamps, savannas, mountains, and deserts in the tropics and subtropics. Different groups of palms exhibit adaptations such as salt tolerance in mangroves, sago starch production, and hurricane resistance.

Many palms take decades to begin flowering and fruiting. Their growth strategy relies on persistent long life over decades or centuries. Some palms, like the Chatham Island Nikau, have endured for over 500 years. Palms thus represent ecological keystone species in their habitats. Their fruits feed birds and mammals. Leaves, sap, and stems provide materials for thatch, textiles, candy, and alcoholic beverages across human cultures.

The banana family Musaceae contains over 1000 species. The most diverse bananas are inedible. Only two species produce the common commercial dessert bananas - Musa acuminata and Musa balbisiana.
Meanwhile, cooking bananas and plantains derives from crosses with other Musa species. Bananas thrive in humid lowland tropics and subtropics as medium-sized pseudostems. The abundance and constant yield of bananas from perennial rhizomes make them a vital carbohydrate source. However, most commercial clones are parthenocarpic and sterile, requiring vegetative propagation. This genetic uniformity leaves banana crops vulnerable to diseases like Fusarium wilt. Breeding programs aim to hybridize cultivated bananas with resistant wild Musa genomes.
The ginger family Zingiberaceae encompasses over 1500 species of aromatic rhizomatous herbs. Gingers thrive in tropical forests, especially the understories of Asia. Zingiberaceae plants contain oils and resins that likely serve as defenses against herbivores and pathogens. The characteristic spicy aroma comes from phenylpropanoids like gingerol. Many gingers also have showy flowers pollinated by specialized birds.
Valued gingers include turmeric, cardamom, and galangal, which are used as spices and traditional medicines. The paradise tree, with huge waxy aromatic blossoms, holds cultural significance across the tropics. Etlingera elatior, or torch ginger, displays one of the largest inflorescences in the plant kingdom. Zingiberaceae diversity provides a wealth of flavors, scents, and ornamentals.
However, habitat loss threatens palm, banana, and ginger families. Palm heart harvesting decimates wild populations. Banana monocultures suffer disease epidemics. Forest degradation harms shade-adapted gingers. Climate change may also reduce the suitability of tropical environments. Conserving the genetic diversity of these important monocot families requires habitat protection and agricultural diversification to ensure their gifts continue enriching human cultures.

Monocot Houseplants and Garden Plants

Beyond their roles in native ecosystems, monocots thrive in commercial gardens. s. Their striking forms, textures, and inflorescences make monocots prized additions indoors and outdoors. This section surveys some of the most common monocot houseplants and garden plants appreciated for their unique beauty.

Several palm species make excellent houseplants. The pygmy date palm (Phoenix roebelenii) remains compact with graceful, feathery green leaves for years. With proper conditions, Majestic Kentia palms (Howea forsteriana) can reach treelike heights over time. The parlor palm (Chamaedorea elegans) and areca palm (Dypsis lutescens) also thrive indoors. Dwarf banana (Musa cavendishii) varieties produce bold tropical foliage. They can also produce fruits and flowers. Palms lend a verdant jungle ambiance to indoor spaces.

Many bromeliads, including pineapple, Spanish moss, and air plants, adapt well to growing in homes and gardens. Their intricate rosettes and spiky foliage add striking shapes and textures. Bromeliads come in a rainbow of leaf colors, from scarlet red to silver blue. Some bromeliads produce exotic inflorescences; others are appreciated for boldly variegated leaves. Most bromeliads only require moderate light and moisture.

Numerous orchids also make stunning houseplants as long as essential care requirements are met. Phalaenopsis and moth orchids bloom freely and tolerate average indoor conditions. Cattleyas, dendrobiums, oncidiums, and cymbidiums also commonly grow indoors, providing their light, humidity, and temperature needs are fulfilled.

Many garden perennials and flowering bulbs come from diverse monocot groups beyond the popular ornamental grasses, lilies, and irises. Dramatic colocasia and alocasia selections feature huge leaves. Gladiolus and crocosmia provide vivid spikes of color. Tropical gingers like Red Torch, Butterfly, and Shell have oversized vivid blooms. Behnia cultivars offer showy foliage and flowers. Water-wise, agaves, and yuccas lend architectural depth.

Exploring monocot diversity yields new gems. Many striking aquatic monocots also thrive in water gardens and aquariums. Lotus flowers come in pink, white, yellow, and red varieties that contrast beautifully with lily pad leaves. Water lilies offer similarly showy flowers floating above underwater foliage. Tropical papyrus forms tall, unique umbels. Iris pseudacorus glows bright yellow in ponds and along streams. Water hawthorns and water snowflakes produce delicate white flowers. Adding diverse water-loving monocots creates serene beauty.

Hardy gardeners can try cultivating more challenging monocots like low-maintenance bamboo or tropical gingers and bananas in frost-free climates. Giant elephant ear leaves make tropical statements. Trying new monocot varieties beyond everyday lilies and irises opens our eyes to amazing diversity. Even learning proper care for orchids and bromeliads allows us to appreciate their marvelous intricacy.

Remember never to collect monocots from the wild. Seek nursery-propagated plants or ethically sourced seeds. Match plants' cultural needs to your growing conditions. Join local orchid, palm, bamboo, or bromeliad societies to gain knowledge from experts. Exchanging divisions with other enthusiasts also spreads beauty. Growing monocots rewards us with unique forms while appreciating the long evolutionary journey that shaped their diversity.

Rare and Endangered Monocots

While monocots comprise some of Earth's most abundant plant species, many monocot groups also contain endangered plants threatened by extinction. Habitat loss, overharvesting, invasive species, and climate change all impact rare monocots. Understanding endangered monocots helps guide conservation priorities. This section surveys some of the most vulnerable rare monocots and efforts to protect them.

The palm family exemplifies the precarious state of many rare monocots. Palms often have small geographic ranges restricted to isolated tropical refuges. Extensive deforestation depletes palm populations and genetic diversity. Nearly 200 palm species are classified as endangered or critically endangered. Pritchardia remota, a palm from the Hawaiian Islands, numbers less than 100 individuals remaining. The Chilean wine palm Jubaea chilensis survives in fragments of its former range—many tropical palm species on the brink lack effective environmental protection.

Orchids also face extensive endangerment, with habitat specialists most at risk. Over 1,000 orchid species are included on the IUCN Red List. Some epiphytic orchids are incredibly rare. Only one specimen of the ghost orchid Eurycles ambohitraensis is known from Madagascar. Other orchids, like the Cuban butterfly orchid Encyclia bocourtii, number fewer than 100 individuals in the wild. These decrees highlight the need for ex-situ conservation efforts. Seed banking can preserve genetic diversity if habitats are restored.

Several monocot genera exhibit exceptionally high rates of endangerment. Zingiberales families like the banana, ginger, and heliconia relatives suffer degradation of their tropical forest homes. Half of all Heliconia species make the IUCN Red List, including the endangered Heliconia spathocircinata, which is only found near a few Brazilian waterfalls. Unsustainable wild harvest also threatens these Zingiberales for medicine or horticulture. Likewise, half of all palm species in Madagascar qualify as endangered or critically endangered. This island's palms require urgent conservation. Grasses may seem ubiquitous, but many specialist species are endangered. Coastal grasses like the European bitter bluegrass face habitat loss to development. Rare endemic grasses grow on unusual serpentine soils. Overgrazing and trampling degrade fragile alpine grasslands. Even widespread prairie grasses suffer genetic erosion as vast uniform stands replace diverse prairies.

Sedges and rushes also decline as wetland drainage continues globally. Bulbous sedge species like Carex depressa require specific vernal pool hydrology and face overwhelming habitat destruction. Desert wetland rushes contend with drought, invasive species, and groundwater depletion. Fragmentation leaves many sedge and rush species vulnerable even where pockets of habitat remain.

Preventing monocot biodiversity losses requires tailored conservation strategies. Habitat protection and restoration maintain native plant communities. Sustainable harvest regulations can balance the use and preservation of monocot resources. Public education fosters appreciation for unique biodiversity like rare orchids and palms. Integrated in-situ and ex-situ approaches are imperative. Conserving tissue samples, seeds, and living collections hedges against extinction.

With focused efforts, diverse monocot lineages can thrive into the future. Grasslands, orchid-filled forests, palm oases, ginger-scented jungles, and lush wetlands have inspired us for millennia. Ensuring monocots continue evolving, adapting, and gracing human cultures with their splendor remains an imperative shared across humanity. The unique gifts of monocot diversity enrich our lives - but conserving them requires proactive commitment. With biological insights and compassion, these exceptional flowering plants will flourish for generations to come.

Chapter 5

Flowering Plants: Eudicots

The Diversity of Eudicots

As one of the two major angiosperm lineages, eudicots display huge species diversity across a vast array of habitats. Estimates suggest over 175,000 species of eudicots exist worldwide. They dominate most temperate and tropical ecosystems. Eudicots diverged from an ancient common ancestor with monocots about 140 million years ago during the Early Cretaceous. Since then, eudicots have undergone rapid diversification and rise to ecological prominence. Understanding what defines eudicots as a whole illuminates their success through evolutionary time.

The eudicot clade is strongly supported by both morphological and molecular evidence. Key anatomical traits differentiate most eudicots from other angiosperm groups. Eudicots possess leaves with branched, net-like vein patterns compared to the parallel veins of monocots. Their flower parts occur in fours or fives, versus monocot flowers, often arranged in threes. Eudicot pollen contains three apertures or pores, contrasting the single pores in most monocot pollen grains.

Within eudicot stems, vascular bundles form a ring shape, with the xylem and phloem tissues arranged in concentric circles. Roots also display xylem arranged in a central cylinder. Overall, eudicots exhibit more complex tissue organization than other angiosperms. This complexity allowed for diversification into trees, shrubs, and herbs with specialized transport tissues enabling large sizes.

While eudicots display vast diversity, DNA evidence identifies shared mutations supporting their common ancestry. All eudicots experienced a whole genome duplication event early in their evolution. This genome multiplication enabled new gene functions and evolutionary flexibility. Phylogenetic trees built using molecular markers consistently unite eudicots as a monophyletic group - containing all descendants from their shared progenitor lineage.

Eudicots comprise over 75% of all flowering plants on Earth today. Major eudicot lineages include rosids, asterids, and ranunculids, which dominate most plant communities. Yet new species and evolutionary relationships are discovered continually, especially in biodiverse tropical regions. Comprehensive eudicot phylogenies remain difficult to resolve. However, anatomical, morphological, and genetic evidence confirm eudicots represent one of the most successful branches of land plant evolution. Eudicots occupy nearly every terrestrial habitat and niche, from alpine tundra to tropical forests. They outcompete other plants in most temperate and tropical regions. Diverse growth forms like trees, shrubs, vines, herbs, and epiphytes all evolved among eudicots. This structural variety, paired with physiological adaptations, enabled eudicots to proliferate.

The pragmatic definition of eudicots relies on shared derived traits, the synapomorphies that mark their monophyletic lineage. However, some exceptions exist where particular eudicots may lack certain typical eudicot characteristics. For example, some plants classified biochemically as eudicots display monocot-like parallel leaf venation or floral parts in threes. These outliers likely represent reversals to ancestral conditions or unique adaptations.

Despite the exceptions, eudicots exhibit consistent tendencies tracing back to their origins over 140 million years ago. The ancestral eudicot genome fostered flexibility and innovation. Following continental drift that isolated plant populations, eudicots diversified via adaptation to new environments and coevolution with animal pollinators and seed dispersers. These bursts of speciation produced the astounding eudicot diversity that still characterizes ecosystems worldwide.

While many eudicot relationships remain uncertain, improved DNA sequencing and computational phylogenetics continue elucidating their evolutionary tree of life. Traditional classification systems based on morphology are giving way to robust clades resolved through molecular evidence. However, much work remains to fully catalog eudicot biodiversity, especially in species-rich locations like tropical rainforests. Each new discovery provides a deeper appreciation for how eudicots came to dominate the planet.

The remarkable story of eudicot success comes into focus by integrating evidence from diverse disciplines. Their anatomical advantages and genetic fertility allowed rapid adaptation. Reproductive innovations like flower and fruit dispersal mechanisms drove coevolution with animals. A history of genome duplications conferred genetic flexibility. Through these advantages, eudicots proliferated to become the globe-spanning diversity we observe today, providing ecological structure and human sustenance.

Roses, Mints, Nightshades, and More

Several major lineages of eudicots fall within the clade Rosids, containing about 70,000 diverse species. Rosids comprise around a third of all eudicot diversity. This section surveys some of the important rosid families, including ecologically and economically significant groups of flowering plants. Understanding rosid diversity provides insight into eudicot evolution and human uses of these plants.

Rosaceae's rose family contains over 3,000 species, including many beloved fruits, flowers, and ornamental plants. Roses, strawberries, raspberries, apples, pears, plums, cherries, peaches, and almonds belong to Rosaceae. Potentilla, spirea, rowan, and hawthorn provide popular garden and landscape shrubs. Certain Rosaceae, like cinquefoils and avens, thrive in alpine habitats. The family displays huge diversity in growth forms, fruits, flower morphology, and habitats.

Square stems and aromatic leaves characterize species in the mint family Lamiaceae. The 7,000 species include many culinary herbs like basil, oregano, thyme, sage, rosemary, and true mints. Lamiaceae also provides medicines, dyes, and ornamentals. This family's drought-tolerant shrubs, perennials, and annuals grow across temperate regions worldwide. Specialized flower shapes and scents reflect adaptations for attracting pollinators.

The nightshade family Solanaceae contains over 2,000 species, including potatoes, tomatoes, peppers, tobacco, petunias, and deadly nightshade. Alkaloids in Solanaceae provide medicinal compounds as well as toxic ones. Species thrive in various habitats, from rainforests to deserts. Solanaceae displays diverse growth forms and flower morphologies specialized for different pollinators. Many genera provide important agricultural crops around the globe. Other economically important rosid groups include the legume, heath, and citrus families. Legumes, or Fabaceae, are the third largest plant family with over 19,000 species, including peas, beans, soybeans, peanuts, and many tropical trees. Legumes form symbiotic nitrogen-fixing root nodules with bacteria, fulfilling crucial ecological roles. The heath family, Ericaceae, provides edible berries, ornamental shrubs like rhododendrons and azaleas, and timber. Citrus fruits, including oranges, lemons, limes, and grapefruit, come from the family Rutaceae, along with aromatic rue herbs.

While offering immense value to humans, these rosids also provide foundational ecological services. Leguminous plants fertilize nutrient-poor soils. Diverse rosid nectar and fruit sources sustain pollinators and seed dispersers. Heathlands and shrublands stabilize landscapes against erosion. The structural variety of rosid growth forms creates ecosystems from rainforest understories to alpine meadows.

Understanding these significant rosids' shared traits and evolutionary origins provides key insights for ecology and economics. Their diversification resulted from adaptations to new habitats and coevolution with pollinators. Convergent evolution also produced similar forms in distant rosid lineages, like Australian protea flowers mimicking European heaths. Maximizing future uses of rosids requires conserving genetic diversity and wild relatives to maintain adaptive potential. Protecting rosid-rich habitats ensures these valuable eudicots continue enriching human lives through beauty, nourishment, and environmental renewal.

Daisies, Sunflowers, Violets, and Asters

The expansive eudicot clade Asterids contains over 80,000 diverse species. This section examines some notable asterid families, including many domesticated ornamentals and crops. Understanding the diversity within Asterids provides insight into eudicot evolution and human selective breeding.

One distinctive asterid family is the daisies, Asteraceae, with over 32,000 species. Also called composites, daisies have dense flower heads containing many individual flowers. Daisies include sunflowers, asters, zinnias, coneflowers, dandelions, and lettuce. This highly adaptable family thrives across habitats worldwide. Daisies exhibit specialized pollen and flower structures facilitating insect pollination. Many genera provide medicines, dyes, fibers, and ornamentals.

The nightshade family Solanaceae, described in the section above, also falls within the asterids. Containing tomatoes, potatoes, peppers, tobacco, and petunias, Solanaceae provides key global crops rich in alkaloid chemicals. Asterids encompass several other agricultural families, like the coffee family Rubiaceae, olive family Oleaceae, and bedstraw family Rubiaceae.

Some asterids thrive in extreme environments, like the salt-tolerant goosefoot family Chenopodiaceae—ephemeral annuals in the daisy genus Gnaphalium pioneer harsh volcanic soils. High alpine cushion plants in Asteraceae survive freezing temperatures and desiccation. Such adaptations result from convergent evolution across asterid lineages.

Gardeners likely grow many asterid ornamentals, including chrysanthemums, dahlias, violets, impatiens, petunias, salvias, and penstemons. These provide ample choices for pollinator gardens that support ecosystem services. Learning botanical connections between these popular flowers highlights how our horticultural choices relate to broader plant ecology and evolution. Beyond crop riches, asterids also provide ecological insights through convergent evolution. For example, cacti in the New World evolved succulent water-storing stems and spines independently from euphorbia succulents in the Old World. Both groups adapted to arid environments by limiting transpiration and deterring herbivores. Such parallels reveal how different lineages follow similar evolutionary trajectories.

Asterids continue diversifying in sometimes surprising ways. The aquatic watermilfoil genus Myriophyllum originated on land but adapted to freshwater ecosystems worldwide. The holoparasite genus Cuscuta in the morning glory family evolved to lack chlorophyll and extract nutrients directly from host plants. These innovations emphasize the flexibility of the asterids.

However, many specialized asterids now face threats. Overharvesting for traditional medicines decimates wild populations of medicinal Rubiaceae trees. Habitat loss threatens the vernal pool and serpentine annuals. Invaders outcompete endemic Hawaiian daisies. But conservationists work to protect important centers of asterid diversity, propagate rare species ex-situ, and restore degraded lands.

Appreciating the astounding diversity and ecological contributions of the asters provides context for the human experience. People evolved surrounded by asterid-dominated habitats providing nourishment, medicine, and beauty. Conserving these invaluable plants remains crucial for culture and ecology, so their gifts persist into the future. Integrating traditional knowledge and scientific insights provides the comprehensive understanding required for long-term asterid conservation.

Legumes, Citrus, Avocados, and Maples

Several other distinctive eudicot families hold major ecological and economic significance for humans. Exploring their shared traits and diversity provides insight into eudicot evolution and human culture. This section surveys notable eudicot groups, including legumes, soapberries, avocados, magnolias, and maples.

The legume family Fabaceae contains over 19,000 species, including peas, beans, soybeans, peanuts, and the locust, mesquite, acacia, and mimosa trees. Many legumes form symbiotic root nodules with nitrogen-fixing rhizobium bacteria, enhancing nutrient-poor soils. Their nutrient-rich seeds have sustained human civilizations for millennia. High in protein, legumes remain staple crops globally today.

The soapberry family Sapindaceae includes lychee and longan fruits, maples, and the paullinia vines used to produce the stimulant drink guaraná. Sapindaceae species thrive in tropical to temperate climates worldwide. Many contain saponins, soapy chemicals providing natural pesticides. The maple genus Acer provides distinctive winged fruits, timber, and, of course, sweet sap.

Avocados belong to the laurel family Lauraceae and are known for aromatic leaves and fruits. Laurels like bay, cinnamon, sassafras, and allspice contribute flavors and medicines. Subtropical Lauraceae trees thrive in cloud forests, including avocados and the gorgeous pink camphor laurel. Camphor distillation provided insect repellents before synthetic chemicals.

Magnolias and tulip trees hold ancestral significance as early flowering eudicot lineages. Magnoliaceae's showy blooms still adorn gardens and forests worldwide. Fossil evidence shows Magnolia-like blossoms existing when dinosaurs still roamed. Surviving as relics emphasizes the resilience of Magnoliaceae evolution over 100 million years. Beyond agriculture, these eudicot groups provide products that enrich human cultures immeasurably. Citrus fruits deliver essential vitamin C to prevent scurvy, enabling naval trade routes. Maple syrup delights palates and pioneers: Camphor and sassafras flavors defined colonial teas and sweets. Guaraná drinks supply caffeine, sustaining indigenous South American communities.

These families also enrich ecosystems ecologically. Legume nitrogen fixation supports plant growth and carbon storage. Lauraceae leaves shed slowly, providing humid forest floor nutrients. Maple-winged fruits spread with the spinning propellers. Sapindaceae saponins may have antifungal and antimicrobial activities benefiting plants. Observing nature reveals their hidden contributions.

Unfortunately, extensive habitat loss now threatens many species within these important eudicot groups. Overharvesting for ornamental magnolia, timber decimated Asian forests. Palm oil plantations replace diverse tropical ecosystems containing Lauraceae and Sapindaceae relatives. Invasive pests target native legumes and maples. Conservation of hotspots, livelihood transitions, and ecological restoration provide hope for protecting remaining diversity.

Common Eudicot Houseplants

While eudicots display astounding ecological diversity outdoors, many genera make excellent houseplants appreciated for decorative foliage or flowers. Understanding optimal care for these popular indoor eudicots provides insights into their adaptations and origins. This section surveys some of the most beloved eudicot houseplant groups and how to help them thrive indoors.

Orchidaceae orchids are currently the top-selling houseplants worldwide due to their amazing flower diversity. While specific care varies by genus, most orchids require bright but indirect light, air circulation, limited potting mix, and well-drained pots. Water thoroughly, then allow orchids to dry between waterings. Special fertilizer at quarter strength prevents salt buildup. Matching natural habitats helps success.

Gesneriaceae African violets have been cherished houseplants for over a century. Their purple, pink, red, and white blossoms flower prolifically with appropriate light. Water when the soil surface becomes dry. Use room temperature water to prevent chilling. Introduce fertilizer at half-strength monthly during growth periods. Yellowed leaves indicate too much or too little water and light. You can also gift plants by repotting attached offshoots.

The coffee family Rubiaceae contains beloved shrubs like Gardenia and Ixora, appreciated for their fragrant white flowers. Gardenias demand bright light, high humidity, and acid soil. Ixoras tolerate more sun but need similar humidity. Yellowing leaves on these Rubiaceae signal insufficient light or nutrients. Prune to encourage bushy growth.

Succulents like Crassulaceae jade plants and cacti are low-maintenance eudicots tolerating benign neglect. Let jade plant soil dry completely between waterings and provide several hours of direct sun. Cacti likewise need a dry interval of 7-10 days and significant sunlight exposure to the flower. Underwatering is safer than overwatering with succulents. Remove offsets for propagation. Foliage plants like Dracaena, Dieffenbachia, and Epipremnum provide vertical architecture and air purification. Dracaena requires moderate light and tolerates missed waterings. Dieffenbachia prefers more moisture but not sogginess. Lovely heart-shaped philodendrons trail gracefully. Wipe dusty leaves occasionally and stake climbing varieties.

The ginseng family Araliaceae contains tropical shrubs like polyscias and schefflera, prized for cut foliage. Provide bright indirect light and humidity. Prune to shape plants as desired. Repot when rootbound, but avoid sudden shifts to much larger containers. Protect scheffleras from chills below 50 degrees Fahrenheit.

Flowering maple in the Malpighiaceae adds vivid color with red, orange, pink, or white blooms against dark green leaves with red veins. Give abundant light and moderate water. Pinch back to encourage bushiness. Flowering maple naturally drops leaves in autumn before growing again in spring.

Understanding eudicot houseplant families and their cultural needs allows us to appreciate the diversity of forms adapted to various environments over millennia. Caring for living plants connects us to nature's marvels, even inside our homes. Responsible enjoyment through propagation and conservation allows these eudicot gifts to enrich future generations.

Notable and Unusual Eudicots

While most eudicots belong to large, familiar families, some unique species stand out through bizarre adaptations or historical significance. Exploring the most eccentric eudicots provides insight into the flexibility of their evolution. This section surveys some of the quirkiest and most remarkable eudicot plants.

The giant corpse flower (Amorphophallus titanum) produces the largest unbranched inflorescence in the plant kingdom, reaching over 10 feet tall. Its unique pseudanthium generates heat and foul odors resembling rotten meat to attract carrion beetle pollinators. This endangered Indonesian aroid has become a botanical celebrity, with blooming events drawing huge crowds at greenhouses.

The enormous disc-like welwitschia plant of the Namib Desert also garners fame for its bizarre appearance and adaptation to harsh conditions. Just two leaves continuously grow from a woody trunk throughout the welwitschia's lifetime, which can exceed 1500 years. The leaves split and frayed into strips to reduce water loss. This relic plant survives in just two arid regions of southern Africa.

Many unusual eudicots exist as botanical curiosities with little apparent survival value. The jabuticaba tree produces fruits directly along its trunk and branches. The flowering banana has a pseudostem that morphs into a large crimson inflorescence. The dragon's blood tree oozes red sap, while the rainbow eucalyptus sheds multicolored bark. These intriguing forms enrich eudicot diversity.

Several eudicots stand out for their great size, including the giant sequoia, eucalyptus, banyan figs, and rubber trees. Coast redwoods can exceed 360 feet tall. Tropical tree species support their enormous heights using buttress roots for stability and water transport. These giants substantially influence forest ecology as keystone species. Their longevity over millennia is humbling. Some remarkable eudicots have no wild populations remaining but continue living as cultural artifacts. The sacred lotus flower figured prominently in ancient Egyptian, Hindu, and Buddhist iconography. No longer found in the wild, the lotus persists cultivated in ponds. The dodo tree faced extinction in Mauritius until conservationists germinated antique seeds found in museum collections. This living relic survives actively conserved.

Certain eudicots stand out for superlative chemical production. The coca plant contains the highest concentration of cocaine in the plant kingdom. Quinine, an antimalarial compound, comes from cinchona bark. Madagascar periwinkle offers over 70 medicinal alkaloids. These pharmaceutical treasures reveal the wealth of eudicot chemodiversity. However, overharvesting for single compounds threatens wild species and traditional uses.

While many bizarre plants offer little direct utility to humanity, their peculiar adaptations provide wonder and inspiration. Unusual eudicots compel us to marvel at the boundless forms evolution can craft. Appreciating their whimsy and rarity kindles compassion to conserve Earth's astounding botanical diversity. Each idiosyncratic eudicot lineage represents millions of years of survival against the odds. These unique plants deserve protection, so their extraordinary stories continue. By spotlighting eccentric eudicot species, we gain a deeper perspective on life's fragility, resilience, and creativity.

Chapter 6
Trees and Shrubs

The Biology and Growth of Trees

Trees are resplendent. They are the largest and oldest individuals in the plant kingdom, with heights over 100 meters and lifespans over 5,000 years. Understanding tree biology provides insights into their towering achievements. This section explores traits enabling trees to grow enormous and endure for millennia.

Unlike herbaceous plants, trees maintain aboveground woody biomass year-round. Their stems undergo secondary growth via vascular cambium, adding girth annually through woody xylem and phloem production. Trees allocate energy into height early to compete for sunlight, then divert resources toward diameter growth and reproduction. This developmental shift causes trunk taper.

Trees cannot survive injuries to cambium, bark, and roots as herbaceous plants can. But longevity trades off with repair ability. Trees also compartmentalize wounds and decay while maintaining healthy tissue function nearby. Their modular organization affords redundancy. Deciduous trees conserve nutrients by translocating minerals from leaves before shedding them in autumn.

An essential adaptation enabling tree height is strengthened cellulose in wood cell walls. Cellulose microfibril orientation changes through secondary xylem layers, optimizing structural support. Trees also produce specialized chemicals called lignin and suberin in wood and cork cells, conferring mechanical strength and water impermeability.

Together, these compounds allow water transport over 300 feet high in giant sequoias. Responding to sway stimulates reaction wood formation for added stability. Trees also use branching architecture and sacrificial dead bark for protection. Trees retain juvenile properties like shade tolerance longer before maturing. This helps saplings persist below the canopy. Indeterminate apical growth also enables height plasticity in response to light competition. Some trees even exhibit resting bud dormancy, pausing until environmental conditions improve.

Root systems provide another essential adaptation. Most trees develop extensive lateral roots, stabilizing the enormous mass aboveground. Taproots offer deep anchorage and access to groundwater in some species, like oaks. Buttress roots along the basal trunk provide structural bracing in large tropical trees.

Mycorrhizal fungal partnerships enhance nutrient and water absorption through the small absorbing rootlets of fine feeder roots. The large surface area of fine roots cannot be sustained without fungal symbionts. In exchange, trees provide sugars to the fungi.

Together, these specializations enable trees to grow exceptionally tall, wide, and old compared to other plants. They fill keystone ecological roles and provide myriad benefits to humanity. But refining our understanding of tree biology continues, especially regarding migration, regeneration, and mortality dynamics. Unlocking the secrets of forest resilience can help conserve these majestic organisms, providing global ecological services.

Notable Tree and Shrub Families

Beyond individual species, understanding the traits of tree and shrub plant families provides insight into their evolution and ecology. This section surveys some of the major woody plant families that dominate forests and landscapes worldwide.

The pine family Pinaceae contains over 200 species of cone-bearing evergreen trees. Pines, firs, spruces, larches, hemlocks, and cedars belong to Pinaceae. They thrive in temperate and boreal climates with drought and cold tolerance. Pinaceae trees often dominate canopies with towering heights of up to 300 feet. They sequester immense amounts of carbon in widespread northern forests.

Myrtle family trees like eucalyptus dominate warmer climates. Myrtaceae contains over 5,500 species of aromatic trees and shrubs with fleshy berries. Eucalypts provide timber, while allspice, clove, and guava offer spices and fruits. Myrtaceae species thrive in tropical and subtropical forests, savannas, and bogs. Distinctive oil glands flavor and protect leaves.

Willows, poplars, and cottonwoods comprise the Salicaceae family of over 400 deciduous trees and shrubs. Salicaceae grow across temperate and boreal biomes worldwide. They favor riparian habitats, stabilizing stream banks with tough, flexible wood. Salicaceae trees offer medicines like salicylic acid that inspired aspirin.

Oaks, beeches, birches, and chestnuts dominate the Fagaceae, or beech family. Over 900 species provide hardwood lumber, tannins, nuts, and wildlife habitat. Fagaceae trees display intricate coevolution with fungal symbionts and animal seed dispersers. The family emerged and diversified during cooling climates over 50 million years.

The soapberry family Sapindaceae, described in section 5.4, contains many tropical trees. Maples, lychees, longans, and locust berries offer prized fruits, woods, and medicines. Sapindaceae occurs across tropical to temperate forests and savannas. Other important tropical tree families include the custard apples, Annonaceae, and the Brazil nut family Lecythidaceae. The mahogany family, Meliaceae, provides prized tropical timber. Many species thrive in seasonally dry forests, tolerating occasional drought after losing leaves. The kapok and baobab trees store water in swollen trunks to survive harsh environments. Even temperate members like the Neem tree withstand hot, arid conditions.

Showy flowering shrubs often dominate family recognition over trees. These include heaths like rhododendrons in the Ericaceae, camellias in the Theaceae, and viburnums in the Adoxaceae. However, most of these families contain tree relatives that provide timber or ecological support.

The pea family Fabaceae, also contains many tropical trees with nitrogen-fixing root nodules. They enrich impoverished soils and provide vital ecosystem resources through seed and foliage production. Yet, little public awareness of important legume timber trees extends beyond mesquite and locusts.

Studying distinctive woody plant families provides insight into the evolution of trees and shrubs across habitats and continents. Comparing family traits and biogeography reveals how lineages adapted over time. Genera tend to associate with consistent, familiar companions linked through shared ecologies. Recognizing these family ties allows deeper awareness of local plant communities.

Observing related species also shows the flexibility of adaptive forms within families. Growth habits, biomechanical properties, and reproductive strategies diverge as genera diversify into new niches. This clandestine variety sustains diverse forest ecosystems. Yet threats from development and climate change now jeopardize many of these woody plant lineages. Conservation of their genetic diversity preserves options for the future.

Using Trees and Shrubs in Landscaping

Beyond ornamental value, incorporating trees and shrubs into landscapes provides many functional benefits. Their myriad services, from climate moderation to wildlife habitat, enhance property utility and pleasure. This section explores considerations when selecting, placing, and caring for landscape trees and shrubs.

Choosing the right plants for the location and conditions ensures success. Consider mature size to avoid overcrowding and excessive pruning needs. Look for native or well-adapted non-invasive species. Match cold-hardiness and drought tolerance to local climate extremes. Prioritize habitat offerings like pollen, nectar, seeds, and shelter. A diversity of trees, shrubs, and understory vegetation creates an ecologically balanced ecosystem.

Placement and spacing affect aesthetics and functionality. Allow ample room for trees to reach mature canopies without encroaching on structures. Cluster small trees and shrubs to create intimate spaces. Use larger specimens as living sculptures. Align plants to frame desirable views or screen eyesores. Position shade trees to cool buildings in summer while allowing winter solar access. Design flow around focal points and destinations.

Incorporating native plants fosters local biodiversity. They support specialized pollinators, herbivores, and fungal associates. Native trees anchor ecosystems, providing nest sites and food sources for birds. Developing plantings in ecological succession, from grasses to shrubs to canopy trees, attracts increasing diversity. Avoid invasive exotics that escape cultivation. Seek local ecotypes and cultivars over generic nursery varieties when possible. Careful tree and shrub selection prevents problems like cracked sidewalks, blocked views, fallen leaves, and excessive pruning –research species' characteristics before planting. Select smaller trees for confined spaces. Avoid shallow-rooted trees for patios or walls. Prevent obstructed sight lines with summer and winter growth habits in mind. Match leaf litter to usage - oaks near play areas, maple and beech beside driveways.

Caring for trees and shrubs ensures their health, safety, and intended functions. Prune to enhance structure, remove deadwood, and allow clearance. Avoid excessive pruning that disfigures natural forms. Monitor for disease and pests, focusing on prevention first. Propagate special species for future replacements. Mulch and irrigate appropriately, especially at planting–stake only when critical for establishment. A little planning and care sustains vibrant, low-maintenance landscapes.

Incorporating thoughtful woody plant selections creates spaces that nurture people and support wildlife. Our homes become havens shaded by breathing giants. Design choices impact air, water, microclimate, and habitats beyond property lines. Hardy natives anchor the local plant community. Ornamentals from distant lands display nature's diversity. The living legacy we cultivate today shapes our environment for generations to come. Our gardens represent our values - with wise planting and care, we express foresight and compassion through our choices.

Caring for Trees and Shrubs

Ensuring the health and longevity of landscape trees and shrubs requires attentive care practices. While woody plants are resilient, stresses can lead to decline or death without preventive maintenance. This section explores how to keep trees and shrubs thriving through proper planting, watering, pruning, and protection methods.

Start care before planting with appropriate species selection and site preparation. Choose plants suited for the light, drainage, and space available. Improve compacted or poor soils with adaptations. Locate plants away from eaves, vents, pipes, windows, and wires, allowing mature clearance. When mature, ensure sufficient space between trees, shrubs, structures, and power lines. Pre-water sites before planting and begin mulching immediately after.

Provide sufficient water during establishment and periods of drought. Soak root zones thoroughly, then allow drying rather than frequent shallow watering. Apply additional mulch to retain moisture. Stake only when completely necessary for flexible trunk development. Leave some leaf litter beneath trees to replenish organic matter and nutrients. Monitor for signs of water stress like wilting, scorching, or curled leaves.

Prune only for defined purposes like structure enhancement, clearance, and deadwood removal. Avoid excessive pruning that disfigures natural forms. Make clean cuts just outside branch collars without leaving stubs. Space cuts along branches rather than removing entire limbs—Disinfect tools between trees to prevent disease spread. Hire certified arborists for major pruning jobs. Remove fire blight-infected branches promptly.

Wrapping young, thin-barked trees prevents rodent and sun damage. Rotate the wrap spirally to avoid girdling. Remove wraps during dormancy after several years once the bark toughens—stake only when essential for trunk stability. Remove stakes after one to two years to strengthen natural anchorage. Monitor for pests like borers, scales, mites, or root fungi. Apply preventive systemic treatments as necessary rather than reactive spraying. Fertilize appropriately during active growth and recovery periods. Excess nitrogen harms soil, plants, and waterways. Targeted micronutrients tailored to symptoms or deficiencies promote vigor. Leave ample mulched areas under trees for organic inputs. Maintain protective mulch rings around trunks, preventing damage.

Monitor for signs of decline like thinning canopy, dead branches, unusual growths, staining, or root decay. Identify the source of decline early for prompt treatment. Sterilize tools between trees when pruning to slow infections. Support beneficial microbes and fungi through composts and mulches. Manage pests sustainably, starting with predators, traps, barriers, repellents, and selective treatments.

Cabling and bracing preserve mature trees with structural defects. Consult certified arborists for assessments, cabling, bracing, lightning protection systems, and hazard mitigation. Get trees routinely inspected for early interventions. Proper tree care ensures generations of benefits provided by long-lived woody plants.

Landscape trees and shrubs thrive for decades or centuries with attentive selection, planting, pruning, and protection. They shelter songbirds, purify air, shade homes, and beautify neighborhoods. A commitment to proper stewardship expresses appreciation for the services rendered by woody plants across their long lifespans. Our small efforts sustain arboreal giants, benefitting communities now and for the future.

Remarkable Trees From Around the World

Beyond ordinary trees in backyards and communities, certain ancient trees and towering specimens from around the world capture our imagination. Many have taken on cultural significance after being silent observers of changing eras for centuries. This section describes some of Earth's most spectacular trees that inspire appreciation.

The giant sequoias of California include the largest individual trees on Earth. General Sherman stands 275 feet tall and over 36 feet in diameter at the base. Sequoias are estimated to be over 2,300 years old; their volume exceeds 1,400 cubic meters. Giant sequoias maintain enormous heft thanks to deep roots tapping hidden groundwater and retaining enormous biomass each year. Their thick fire-resistant bark protects from even intense blazes.

Coast redwoods once covered vast areas along the Pacific coast. Today, small remnants remain, including 379-foot tall Hyperion, the tallest living tree measured. Redwoods develop narrow conical crowns to compete for sunlight. Shallow root systems interconnect and layer to stabilize enormous heights. Redwood lumber is prized for its beauty and workability. Only 5% of original old-growth redwood forests endure after extensive logging.

The massive baobabs of Africa and Australia, up to 95 feet thick, also rank among the most massive trees. Their bulbous trunks store water during harsh, dry seasons. Large baobabs can hold over 100,000 liters of water - vital in hot desert climates. Arab legends suggest evil spirits confined inside baobab trunks cause their misshapen gnarly forms. The Sunland Baobab in South Africa features a hollow large enough for 40 people inside its trunk.

The wide-spreading canopies of oak trees made them revered in many cultures. Mighty oak lineages persist across the Northern Hemisphere, some surviving over 1,000 years. Majestic live oaks of the southern United States serve as cornerstone species in savanna ecosystems. Lebanon counts over two dozen ancient oak groves as national monuments. The Wye Oak in Maryland stood over 96 feet tall and nearly 23 feet around before falling during a storm in 2002.

The banyan figs of Asia include the largest single trees by canopy size, spreading laterally indefinitely via aerial prop roots. A giant banyan in Calcutta covers over five acres in the area. Banyans often get planted at village centers in India to provide gathering places. The cobra banyan in Oahu originally had 16 trunks, named for its winding prop roots. Banyans appear in Buddhist and Hindu art as symbols of eternity and divinity.

The giant sequoia is an evergreen conifer that lives up to 3,200 years, making it one of the longest-living organisms on Earth. Native to the western slopes of California's Sierra Nevada mountains, these massive trees reach heights over 300 feet with trunk diameters up to 30 feet. Their enormous size is attributed to the thick, spongy bark that protects them from forest fires. The bark can be over 2 feet thick, allowing the trees to survive even intense wildfires. Giant sequoias are identified by their unique scaly needles and egg-shaped cones. These towering trees play an important ecological role in their native habitat. Their shade provides cooler temperatures for wildlife, while their foliage offers nesting sites. When they shed needles and cones, this litter enriches the soil. Giant sequoias usually grow at elevations between 5,000 and 8,000 feet, forming beautiful groves in California's Sierra Nevada. Several state and national parks protect these areas so people can experience the grandeur of these ancient trees. Their size and age have made them symbols of longevity, perseverance, and the natural wonder of California.
The dragon's blood tree earned its name from its dark red sap, which resembles dried blood when it oozes from damaged bark. Native to the Socotra archipelago off the coast of Yemen, this unusual tree has a distinct umbrella shape formed by its densely packed branches with draping leaves at the tips. Its bark resembles crocodile skin, while its small white flowers cluster into round fruits. The dragon's blood tree thrives in arid conditions, storing moisture in its bulbous trunk, which can be up to 33 feet thick. The trunk's girth helps reduce surface area exposure to dry air and prevents water loss. This allows the tree to survive on only 12 inches of rainfall annually. Local legend claims the trees sprang from the blood of slain dragons, giving rise to its evocative common name. The dragon's blood tree's landscape is characterized by bizarre plant life, earning Socotra recognition as one of the most alien places on Earth. This remarkable island ecosystem has remained isolated for millions of years. Several conservation groups are working to protect Socotra's rare flora and fauna from increased tourism and development.

The majestic banyan tree's aerial prop roots grow into woody trunks, enabling it to spread laterally as it matures. Native to India, the banyan represents long life and has been cultivated for over 1,500 years. When fully grown, this massive tree can cover several acres with its canopy, making it a key shade provider in hot tropical climates. The banyan's prop roots drop from branches and eventually reach the ground, thickening over time. These auxiliary trunks support the wide span of the banyan's crown, allowing it to keep expanding outward. The tree produces an intricate latticework of roots around its core. The branches themselves can grow into epiphytic plants or dangling vines. The banyan's adaptive growth gives the tree an otherworldly appearance. The banyan's expansive, mysterious nature has inspired many cultural legends and folklore. Banyan trees have been historically used as community gathering spaces in India, providing shade for large assemblies. Even today, these majestic trees are honored and protected for their heritage. Their longevity as urban green spaces highlights the importance of maintaining and celebrating natural giants.

The Montezuma cypress is a massive deciduous conifer that can reach heights of 130 feet with trunk diameters up to 11 feet. It is native to Mexico's Oaxaca Valley, representing one of Earth's oldest tree species. Fossil evidence indicates Montezuma cypress trees thrived up to 35 million years ago, meaning they originated during the late Cenozoic era when mammals began to dominate the planet. Today, only a scattered 500 Montezuma cypresses remain in small groves within their native wetland habitat. Their rarity makes them a top conservation priority. An unusual feature of the Montezuma cypress is its ability to regenerate through basal sprouting. When flood waters erode the soil around its base, auxiliary trunks sprout from the exposed roots. This allows the tree to survive catastrophic events and prolongs its lifespan. The furrowed reddish-brown bark also resists wildfires and protects the inner wood. Although harvest and drainage of wetland waters threaten its limited habitat, ongoing efforts aim to preserve Mexico's remaining groves of this tenacious ancient tree. Its endurance intrigues researchers and underscores the biological treasures still being discovered.

The baobab tree of Africa's savanna is scientifically known as Adansonia for its unusual upside-down appearance. The baobab has a bottle-shaped trunk that can exceed 30 feet in diameter, making it one of the most massive trees on the continent. Its branches resemble gnarled roots spreading outwards. This eccentric silhouette gives it the nickname " the upside-down tree." Native to arid regions of Madagascar, mainland Africa, and Australia, the baobab has adapted to seasonal droughts and harsh heat. Their swollen, fire-resistant trunks store water during the rainy months for use during prolonged dry periods. Hollows in mature baobabs can hold hundreds of gallons of water. These reservoirs help support the trees and local wildlife that depend on the baobab for survival. Other useful adaptations include their carotene-packed fruit and vitamin-rich leaves, which people utilize for food and natural medicine. The long-living baobab is intertwined with local culture. These iconic trees can live over 2,000 years, earning them revered status in African folklore as mystical meeting places or ancestral sites. From nourishing communities to representing endurance, the mighty baobab captivates those drawn to its colossal presence.

The tule tree, also known as the Montezuma bald cypress, stands as an ancient natural wonder along Mexico's tropical waterways. Reaching 130 feet tall and up to 40 feet in circumference, the tule tree's wide base and buttressed roots are a magnificent sight. Its scientific name, Taxodium mucronatum, honors the ancient Aztec leader Montezuma, highlighting this tree's long cultural importance. The tule tree once formed expansive freshwater wetland forests across Mexico's lowlands. Today, it is endangered in the wild but remains a national symbol of strength and connection to the past. The broad crowns provide vital habitat for wildlife, while local Cahita peoples still craft canoes from the wood. The knobby "knees" formed above the roots aided oxygen exchange when ancient stands were flooded. Modern conservation efforts aim to preserve the tule tree's remaining groves and saplings, recognizing its ecological and cultural heritage. Although exaggerated legends tell of sacrificial rituals or battle meetings at the feet of a gigantic singular "Tree of Tule," the living tule tree remains an icon of Mexico's landscape. Its endurance through centuries is a testament to nature's surprising resilience, even in the face of modern threats.

Chapter 7

Flowering Herbaceous Plants

Annuals, Biennials, and Perennials

Annuals are flowering herbaceous plants that complete their entire lifecycle within one growing season. After germinating from seed, annuals undergo rapid growth, flowering, pollination, and seed production before dying off when temperatures cool. Some well-known annual flowers include marigolds, zinnias, sunflowers, cosmos, and snapdragons. Annuals are useful for adding quick, vibrant color to gardens. They establish rapidly from seeds sown directly in garden beds after the final frost. Annuals bloom heavily during their single season of growth, with most varieties flowering from early summer through the first frost in fall. When selecting annuals for planting, gardeners should consider their hardiness zone, site conditions, and desired bloom time to ensure success. Short-lived annuals can be started indoors for earlier blooms after transplanting outdoors. Maintaining consistent moisture and removing spent blossoms will promote ongoing flower production. At the end of the season, allowing annuals to self-seed can provide an attractive natural display the following year.

Biennials grow foliage and store energy their first year, then flower, set seed, and die the second year. Common biennial plants include hollyhocks, foxgloves, and lunaria. Gardeners often sow biennials indoors for transplanting later. The young biennial plants require a full growing season in their initial year to establish roots and build food reserves over winter. They form a basal rosette of leaves during this phase and little vertical growth. After overwintering and the return of warmer weather, biennials rapidly shoot up flower stalks. This second season of growth culminates in nectar-rich blooms that attract pollinators for reproduction before the plant dies back. Biennials produce lovely flowers, but their lifecycle means they disappear after seeding. Planting new crops of biennials every year or two will maintain their presence in the garden. Allowing some to self-seed also provides a natural means of propagation.

In contrast to short-lived annuals and biennials, perennials are long-living herbaceous plants. They persist for multiple growing seasons, often flowering annually after reaching maturity. Dividing perennials by root cuttings or transplantation rejuvenates aging plants and yields more for planting. Popular perennial blossoms like peonies, irises, and daylilies continue reappearing yearly once established. Late summer or fall is an ideal time to plant or divide perennials so their roots develop before winter dormancy. Perennials form the backbone of many flower gardens thanks to their reliable return and low maintenance compared to replanting annuals. Designing beds with a diverse blend of perennials with different bloom times extends floral interest across the seasons. While perennials persist year after year, pruning spent flowers and leaves and providing protection in winter helps maintain their health and productivity.

The lifespan differences between annuals, biennials, and perennials play a key role in their cultivation. Annuals rapidly progress through their lifecycle in one season, offering quick bursts of color. Biennials take two years to flower and die, providing interesting but ephemeral blooms. Perennials are the workhorses of the flower garden, blooming repeatedly for many seasons with proper care. Gardeners utilize all three types to create dynamic beds and borders. Knowing the lifespan, needs, and propagation method of each ensures success. Early and late blooming annuals extend floral displays at the margins of the growing season. Biennials add unique blossoms in their second year. Meanwhile, herbaceous perennials form the garden's backbone, providing reliable color and texture year after year; combining all three results in an evolving landscape that balances consistency with periods of delightful change.

The diverse palette of annual, biennial, and perennial flowers allows gardeners to shape herbaceous beds to match their personal vision. Vibrant annuals like zinnias, petunias, and California poppies create intense color impact within a single season. Biennials, including hollyhocks and foxgloves, add stately architectural forms before scattering offspring for next year's display. Reliable perennials like peonies, irises, and phlox persist as garden mainstays while evolving through seasonal succession. Dynamic plantings unfold throughout the growing year by artfully blending all three types. Annuals and biennials fill gaps between perennials, providing waves of new blossoms as different species come into bloom. The interplay between plants with short or long lifespans makes each year unique. Gardeners can also shape species composition over time by encouraging reseeding successors. Understanding herbaceous plants' growth habits and lifespans grants creative license to craft plantings that transform through the seasons.

The versatility of annuals, biennials, and herbaceous perennials makes them suitable for diverse garden settings. Beds and borders allow colorful mixing and matching to create aesthetically pleasing designs. Carefully selected species thrive in specific conditions like shade, drought tolerance, or cottage-style charm. Annuals and biennials work beautifully interplanted with bulbs and woody ornamentals. Containers and window boxes filled with these plants add ornamental portability. Annual vines and trailing types like morning glories, nasturtiums, and sweet peas can soften fences and arbors. Rock gardens and edge plantings benefit from low, spreading perennials. Mixed lifespans give structure yet spontaneity. Whether planted formally or allowed to self-sow, annuals, biennials, and perennials beautify outdoor spaces with possibilities limited only by the gardener's imagination. Their diversity across genera and species promises floral resources to meet any garden vision. When designing gardens featuring annuals, biennials, and herbaceous perennials, considerations like bloom time, color, and height allow for endless creativity. Gardeners can craft dynamic beds by combining early, mid, and late-season bloomers. For example, tulips and bleeding hearts herald spring alongside pansies and forget-me-nots. As spring fades, these are replaced by foxgloves, peonies, and bearded irises blooming in early summer. Later in summer, enjoy dahlias, echinacea, and rudbeckia before chrysanthemums and ornamental kales welcome fall. Blending flowering plants with different lifespans creates a rolling wave of blossoms for nonstop color.

In addition to bloom succession, gardeners can repeat certain hues or contrast colors for visual impact. Warm shades like red canna lilies and orange Mexican sunflowers radiate against a backdrop of cool purple Japanese anemones and asters. Silver-blue hosta leaves illuminate neighboring pastels while providing foliage contrast. Alternating heights also add depth and layers. Tall larkspur and hollyhocks rise above mid-level phlox and painted daisies, which surround low-growing sweet alyssum and verbena. Using annuals and biennials to fill spaces between perennials prevents bare spots while allowing redesign each year. Whether matching or mixing colors and heights, the possibilities are endless.

When designing herbaceous plantings, another consideration is foliage and texture contrasts. Large ruffled hosta leaves differ greatly from nearby fern fronds and dwarf turf lilies. Silver-haired lamb's ear and golden creeping Jenny shimmer bright against green neighbors. Plants like flowering kale and cabbage provide unique leaf shapes and hues. Foliage plants also help fill spaces once spring bulbs have died back. Mixing leaf forms, colors, and textures creates rich visual appeal. Alongside diverse blooms, foliage plants enhance combination plantings: thoughtful plant selection and arrangement results in thematic displays. A cottage garden's informal mix of self-sowing annuals and perennials differs greatly from a meticulous color-coordinated formal bed. But both can be artistically executed using the full palette of flowering herbaceous plants.

Climate considerations also guide decision-making to select plants matched to local growing conditions. Annuals and perennials suited to hot, humid climates differ from alpine varieties requiring cooler temperatures. Mediterranean herbs thrive in drought tolerance, while marsh-loving irises need constant moisture. Maximizing success involves choosing plants compatible with soil, sunlight, and hardiness limitations. Sturdy black-eyed Susans flourish in challenging, dry, poor soils, while delicate impatiens prefer richer, moist shade. Checking tags for sun exposure and zone compatibility prevents mismatches. Gardeners can also expand plant diversity by providing microclimates through sheltered beds, amended soils, or irrigated sections. Taking climate and microclimate into account allows tailored plant combinations. A thoughtfully designed garden playing to its strengths becomes a place where plants naturally thrive.

Finally, the uses of herbaceous plants guide their selection and placement. Fragrant sweet alyssum and lavender line pathways, while canna lilies and bananas lend an exotic flair to tropically inspired beds. Elegant delphiniums and lilies combine in formal displays. Cottage gardens utilize self-sowing annuals and heirloom varieties with casual charm. Plants like sages and mints find culinary uses. Dwarf varieties and cascading plants work beautifully in container gardens and window boxes. Identifying desired uses beautifies specific areas, creates ambiance, or improves utility. Gardeners artfully combine annuals, biennials, and perennials to serve required purposes, whether fragrance, edibility, or simple floral whimsy. By considering all aspects from bloom succession, color, height, and foliage to local adaptability and intended use, gardens speak the creative vision of the gardener.

Annuals, biennials, and perennials allow gardeners to enjoy evolving floral displays that change with the seasons. After establishment, perennials persist year after year as long-term cornerstones. Complementing these, gardeners can reshape annual and biennial accents yearly for fresh infusions of color. Instead of static plantings, herbaceous beds transform through the seasons. Annuals and biennials can be swapped yearly to alter combinations and experiment with new varieties. Allowing some to self-seed introduces delightful spontaneity and natural succession. Where perennials leave gaps after flowering, annuals and biennials plug openings to provide ongoing blossoms and foliage. Their diversity across families, species, and cultivars provides endless options to refresh beds each season. With a palette of short-lived and persistent plants, gardens become dynamic works of living art.

Thoughtfully designed annual and perennial beds provide sustenance and habitat for local ecosystems. Contrasting flower forms support diverse pollinator species that forage nectar and transport pollen from one plant to another. The succession of blooms across the seasons ensures food sources are always available. Foliage plants like hostas also provide food for larval butterflies and moths. Allowing spent plants to stand over winter provides seeds for birds and shelter for beneficial insects. Organic soil practices avoid chemical pollutants that are deadly to fragile invertebrates. With biodiversity as a guiding principle, gardens can sustain wildlife. Gardens combine beauty with stewarding nature's intricate interdependencies by understanding plant lifecycles and ecologies.

Annual, biennial, and perennial flowers connect people more intimately with regional climates and the natural world. Participating in each stage of the annual garden cycle fosters awareness of seasonal rhythms. Gardeners' empiric knowledge deepens through ongoing observation, experimentation, and interaction with diverse plants. Patterns emerge as the same species sprout, flower, and fade year after year in tune with seasonal change. Tuning into these lifecycles rather than fighting natural cycles creates more resilient plantings and cultivates patient wisdom. Emulating healthy ecosystems results in greater balance. Whether through biodiversity, holistic experience, or sustainable practices, herbaceous gardeners find meaning through connecting more deeply to plants and local habitats.

Growing Conditions for Herbaceous Plants

Successfully growing the diverse array of herbaceous flowering plants requires meeting their essential requirements for light, water, nutrients, and climate suitability. By understanding a plant's optimal conditions and adapting care practices, gardeners can create an ideal environment for healthy growth and lush blossoms. Light levels play a foundational role in the vigor and flowering of herbaceous plants. Most annuals and perennials thrive best in full sun, meaning at least six hours of direct sunlight daily. Full sun fuels active photosynthesis needed for robust growth. Some plants like petunias, marigolds, and Black-eyed Susans tolerate partial shade but produce less prolific blooms. Others require shade for cooler soil and air, including impatiens, begonias, and ferns. Monitoring sunlight patterns in garden beds guides appropriate plant selection and placement. Providing supplemental light via reflectors or plant moving allows flexibility.

In addition to adequate sunlight, herbaceous plants require sufficient water for transportation, nutrient absorption, cooling, and cellular hydration. Moisture needs vary widely by species. Traditional garden flowers like geraniums, lavender, and coreopsis prefer well-drained soils and tolerate some drought once established. Succulents and cacti thrive in arid, sandy soils. On the other end, moisture lovers like astilbe, ligularia, and Knockout roses demand constant dampness. Most herbs favor moderate moisture-retentive soils. Observing drainage patterns, installing catch basins, and amending soil help expand plant options. Thick mulches conserve moisture, while porous clay soils may need supplementing with compost to retain water. Matching plants to soil moisture levels prevents waterlogging or desiccation.

Providing balanced nutrients tailored to each plant also bolsters health and flowering performance. Most annuals and perennials grow best in slightly acidic to neutral pH loam soils rich in organic matter. Compost, aged manure, leaf mold, and sphagnum peat help build ideal garden soil. Macro and micronutrients are supplied via organic fertilizers applied at planting and reapplied periodically when blooming slows. Herbaceous plants are sensitive to overfertilizing, which causes excessive foliage at the expense of flowers. Targeted supplemental feeds like calcium for delphiniums or iron for dianthus prevent specific deficiencies. Soil tests help gauge pH and nutrient levels, revealing any need for amendments to optimize conditions. With ideal soils and judicious fertilizing, herbaceous plants thrive.

Planting annuals and perennials suited to the garden's specific hardiness zone improves success and longevity. Zones indicate the average coldest temperature each region experiences. Tender plants only hardy to zones 8-9 will persist as perennials in the warmer southern states while succumbing to winter die back further north. Gardeners can expand variety by providing insulated raised beds, cold frames, or indoor overwintering storage for less hardy material. Knowing the target zones of selection prevents disappointing losses. Some useful annuals like cosmos, morning glories, and chamomile readily self-seed, allowing natural selection of the best adapted. Also key is timing the last spring and first fall frosts to guide planting schedules. Attention to zones, microclimates, and frost dates leads to smart plant choices. With favored conditions met, herbaceous plants generously return the gift of radiant blossoms.

Gardeners must also evaluate growing factors like wind exposure, seasonal rainfall, humidity, and altitude when selecting herbaceous plants. Moisture-loving asters thrive in the humid southeast while struggling in arid western deserts. Mediterranean herbs like rosemary, lavender, and thyme prosper in hot, dry conditions but need winter shelter in northern zones. High-elevation mountain gardens favor alpine plants not suited for hotter coastal areas. Wind protection is critical for delicate vines and tall species prone to storm damage. Choosing native species or those originating from regions with similar climates aids success. Beyond zoning and hardiness, adapting to regional and local growing conditions allows any area to support diverse floriferous herbaceous plants. Site analysis and plant selection focused on matching environmental factors can help prevent frustration and disappointment down the road.

With the right plant in the right place, herbaceous species generously reward the gardener with their intended beauty. But the quest does not end at planting. Performing seasonal maintenance focused on each plant's requirements nurtures success. Monitoring for pest or disease issues promptly treats problems before they escalate. Timely pruning, division, and thinning keep plants vigorous. Applying nutritious compost and mulch on a seasonal basis replenishes the soil. Watering attentively through droughts prevents stress while allowing drainage during rains avoids oversaturation. A watchful gardener's care stewarding favorable conditions enables herbaceous plants to shine as desired. The artistry is realizing the beautiful potential of each plant by understanding and meeting its needs.

Beyond setting up ideal growing conditions, gardeners can boost success by properly caring for herbaceous plants through each phase of growth. Starting seeds or transplanting seedlings at the right time allows sufficient growth before flowering. Based on their maturation rate, annuals and vegetables are directly sown after frost danger passes. Earlier starters like cool-weather lettuce, peas, and pansies precede warm-season zinnias, tomatoes, and basil. Biennials and perennials need time to establish roots before winter, so sow or plant these in late summer or early fall. Consulting regional guides times plantings for local conditions.

Providing attentive early care is crucial for seedlings and new plantings. Sheltering tender shoots prevents damage while adequate water and light nurture growth. Thinning or transplanting reduces competition once germinated seeds sprout. Cutting off spent blooms, termed deadheading, promotes reblooming. Applying organic mulch conserves moisture and suppresses weeds. Timely pinching, staking, and pruning shape plants while preventing lodging and opening air circulation. Watchful preventive care in the early weeks and months prevents setbacks and builds vigor. With a strong start, herbaceous plants soon grow resilient.

Midseason care sustains healthy, productive plants once established. Continued weeding and mulching keep growth on track by minimizing stress and competition. Regular deep watering during drought encourages extensive root zones. Adjusting support features accommodates growth. Pruning maintains desired shapes and flowering habits. Pinching back leggy annuals and deadheading faded blossoms channels energy into new buds.

Division and thinning of biennials and perennials prevent overcrowding while providing new plants. Monitoring for pests or diseases allows early intervention. Midseason care focused on needs tailored to each plant's growth habits ensures success. Consistent attention leads to an abundant display of radiant color.

As the season wanes, shifting care prepares plants for dormancy or next year's garden. Allowing annuals and biennials to self-sow before clearing beds propagates hardy offspring. Collecting and storing seeds gathers genetic resources. Leaving dried seed heads and stems provides winter food and shelter for birds. Trimming back leggy growth restores shape and productivity. Ceasing fertilization and reducing water for most plants hardens off tissue for colder weather. Pruning herbaceous perennials prevents disease and dying foliage from marring upcoming growth. Mulching beds insulates roots and replenishes nutrients. Moving containers and lifting tender bulbs provide overwintering protection. Even as the garden fades, thoughtful season-end care promises a bountiful return.

Adapting maintenance practices to the seasonal rhythms of short-lived and enduring herbaceous plants sustains their performance year after year. Annuals and biennials replenish themselves through prolific self-sowing, while perennials require active propagation by division, cuttings, or separation. Continuous multi-season care tailored to each plant's needs keeps specimens healthy and vigorous. Allowing aging plants to renew through self-sowing or division preserves diversity. Supporting nature's cycles of dormancy and regeneration helps herbaceous plants thrive. Working in partnership with the lifespans and growth habits of annuals, biennials, and perennials brings the garden to fruition.

Thoughtful planting schemes intermingle annuals, biennials, and perennials to create layered successional displays. Emerging bulbs like tulips and daffodils precede showy lupines, irises, and peonies. As these fade, coreopsis, daisies, and dahlias carry color through summer. Chrysanthemums and asters extend the finale into fall. Weaving cool and warm season, bloomers provide ongoing blossoms. Annuals fill spaces between perennials, ensuring continuous flowers and foliage. Coordinating heights adds complementary dimension and contrast. Blending forms and colors creates pleasing compositions. Botanists find that Interplanting early starters, midseason performers, and late bloomers results in evolving floral designs that unfold in beauty throughout the seasons.

This sequencing carries over into coordinating bloom times across sun and shade gardens. Morning sun perennials like Columbine and Bleeding Hearts occupy shade beds, while afternoon sun lovers like echinacea and rudbeckia populate sunnier locales. Dappled light supports diverse choices like foxglove and lily-of-the-valley. Gradual successional blooming weaves connective beauty between contrasting exposures. Herbaceous plants also transition gardens between landscapes. Low growers along edges soften the intersection of beds with lawns. Creeping phlox and sweet alyssum cloak rock walls while Verbascum and hollyhocks stand tall as living fences. Thoughtful placement and succession truly integrate herbaceous plants to harmonize garden spaces.
Annuals and herbaceous perennials also inject flexibility into decorative container designs. Changing out annuals provides fresh color combinations on porches and patios. Shearing back spent perennials rejuvenate pots for extended beauty. Spilling trailers like petunias, million bells, and ivy geraniums adorn mixed borders and soften the edges of ornamental containers. Accent plants like parsley and basil serve culinary usefulness. Shifting potted flower arrangements between indoors and outdoors multiplies their impact. The diversity and versatility of annuals and perennials offer myriad creative options for moveable container displays. Their unique growth habits lend themselves beautifully to embellishing spaces temporarily or all season long.

Popular Garden Flower Families

The expansive diversity of flowering herbaceous plants provides endless options to incorporate beauty and utility into gardens. Some of the most beloved and familiar flowering species belong to these iconic families.
The rose family, or Rosaceae, includes countless popular ornamental and edible plants. Roses themselves exhibit incredible variety in flower size, color, and form across climbing, bush, and ground cover types. The heritage rose class offers antique blooms with rich fragrance. Fruiting shrubs like spirea, potentilla, and cotoneaster contribute to four-season interest. Herbaceous perennials such as lady's mantle, bee balm, and soapwort add whimsical blossoms. Culinary favorites like strawberries, raspberries, apples, and almonds also belong to this family. The versatility of Rosaceae makes it indispensable in gardens.

Few families offer more profuse summer blooms than the daisy family or Asteraceae. Abundant garden flowers like sunflowers, daisies, asters, coneflowers, and zinnias showcase this group's diversity of form, color, and size. Daisies symbolize innocence and simplicity with their delicate petals, while stately sunflowers inspire joy and warmth. Many plants in Asteraceae have herbal and medicinal uses, including chamomile, yarrow, echinacea, and feverfew. This beloved family produces cheerful floral displays from spring until autumn's first frosts.

The mint family, Lamiaceae, brings fragrance along with flowers. Lavender, rosemary, thyme, bee balm, and other aromatic herbs come from this group. Showy flowers ranging from salvia's vivid hues to daisy-like perovskia blossoms add visual impact to herb beds. Mint's fast-spreading nature requires some control. But its menthol-scented leaves and pretty blooms perfume gardens and teas. The flowers, foliage, and scents of Lamiaceae powerfully stimulate the senses.

Brassicaceae, the mustard family, contains ornamentals like wallflowers, honesty, alyssum, stock, and vegetable staples such as broccoli, kale, and cabbages—cheerful cool-season blooms in whites, purples, and sunny yellows welcome spring. The foliage of Brassicaceae comes in diverse forms, from frilly kale to purple-veined ornamental cabbages. These plants thrive in early spring and fall, going dormant in the summer heat. Culinary types offer nutritious edible leaves and flowers. The mustard family brings versatility spanning ornamental borders to kitchen gardens.

With dramatic spires up to 6 feet tall, the snapdragon family Plantaginaceae brings stately architecture. The common name snapdragon comes from the dragon-like spotted throats of Antirrhinum majus flowers when gently squeezed. This genus includes perennials, annuals, and trailing types in vibrant red, pink, yellow, and white shades. Plantaginaceae also includes ornamental groundcovers like creeping Veronica and Veronicastrum with tapered spikes. The tall blooms of Plantaginaceae make striking vertical statements in garden beds and borders.

The nightshade or Solanaceae family contains diverse flowering herbs, vines, and shrubs, both beautiful and utilitarian. Floriferous favorites like petunias, browallia, and nicotiana offer profuse blooms in vivid hues. Ornamental peppers provide colorful fruit. Climbing vines, potato vines, and cypress vines lend vertical drama. Many genera contain edible species, including tomatoes, eggplants, peppers, and tomatillos. Though nightshades are quite useful, some contain potent alkaloids, like mandrake and belladonna. When grown with care, this versatile family brings charm along with harvest.

Prolific annual flowering like pansies, violas, and Johnny-jump-ups make Violaceae a favorite garden. These cheerful edible blossoms thrive in cool weather, blooming abundantly in spring and fall. Pansies exhibit incredible diversity with faces in solid, bicolor, and tricolor patterns. Violas include sweet violets, tufted violets, mini violas, and violas ideal for containers. Johnny-jump-ups naturalize with ease. The edible flowers and heart-shaped foliage of Violaceae add playful touches to gardens and salads.

The legume or Fabaceae family is beloved for fragrant and colorful pea blossoms. Sweet peas and lupines offer spikes of pealike blooms useful as cut flowers. Ornamental shrubs add structure, including Mexican bush lupine and indigo. Clover makes an attractive living groundcover. Many legumes enrich the soil by fixing nitrogen, and beans and peas offer nutritious edible seeds. With their high protein content, legumes are beneficial companion plants that help nourish surrounding crops. Their beauty and utility make legumes a treasured family.

Showy foxglove blossoms on towering spires give Plantaginaceae a unique architectural quality. This family includes the common foxglove, Digitalis purpurea, alongside elegant gloves like Digitalis parviflora with dainty orange-speckled flowers. Foxgloves contain cardiac glycosides useful in medicine but are quite toxic if ingested. However, they can add a graceful vertical element to partially shaded beds. Related penstemons like Firebird penstemon offer similar floral spikes in fiery shades. With proper care, Plantaginaceae provides bold accents.

Abundant daisy-like blossoms characterize plants in the aster or Asteraceae family. Summer and fall favorites like coneflowers, zinnias, marigolds, and chrysanthemums hail from this beloved group. Asteraceae includes a high number of herbaceous perennials like blanketflower and coreopsis, prized for their recurrent blooms. Many genera boast cultivars in a diverse spectrum of sizes and colors. The cheerful, abundant blossoms of asters complement most planting schemes. Their diversity makes them indispensable for flower gardens and borders.

The wide variety found across these and other flowering plant families provides the palette to paint beautiful landscapes. Gardeners can recreate cottage charm, formal parterres, prairie meadows, or rock gardens by selecting members from the best families suited to their personal vision. Nature offers inspiration through these time-honored flowering groups passed down through generations of cultivation. Drawing on this inheritance and artfully composing with flowering families creates garden art resonant with botanical history.

Using Herbaceous Plants in Borders and Beds

With proper design and care, herbaceous flowering plants transform gardens into living artworks. Several key considerations create borders and beds that harmonize beauty with purpose. Thoughtful plant selection suited to site conditions ensures success. Composing variations of color, height, and form results in appealing displays. Mixing flowering cycles extends seasonal interest. Repeating colors or contrasts unify the design. Finally, choosing plants that serve intended roles, like fragrance or pollinator habitat, improves utility. Gardeners can fully express their creative vision with the mindful placement of compatible flowering plants.

The first step in planning borders and beds is choosing plants adapted to the garden's growing conditions. Matching light and moisture levels prevents struggling plants. For example, shade beds would incorporate impatiens, astilbe, and ferns, while sun-loving lavender, marigolds, and zinnias populate a hot, dry border. Testing soil pH and amending as needed optimizes nutrition. Considering the climate and microclimates also prevent mismatches, an alpine succulent bed needs different plants than a humid perennial border. Selecting plants naturally suited to the garden's unique environment ensures they will readily flourish.

Another consideration is including early, mid-, and late-season bloomers to extend interest through the seasons. Spring bulbs like tulips and daffodils awaken first, followed by irises, peonies, and lupines in early summer. Coreopsis, zinnias, and roses shine midsummer until asters, sedums, and chrysanthemums close the year. Mixing cool and warm season annuals fills gaps for continuous color. Complementing early bloomers with later perennials results in evolving displays that progress in waves of floral beauty.

Repeating or contrasting blossom colors also creates appealing effects. Monochromatic beds utilizing shades like lavender hosta, astilbe, and violas make serene color echoes. Juxtaposing complementary hues like yellow coreopsis, purple salvia, and pink roses achieves vibrant results. Value contrasts like pale blue alyssum under deep blue delphiniums lends dimensional impact. Grouping analogous colors like orange, yellow, and red sunflowers and marigolds evokes warmth. Thoughtful blending and placement intensify color relationships to unify plantings. Garden beds and borders come alive when thoughtfully designed with contrasting flower forms. Tall vertical spikes of larkspur and delphiniums tower over medium daisies, coreopsis, and red valerian. Mixed heights establish layered dimensions—Intersperse low growers like sweet alyssum and creeping phlox around medium plants' feet to build depth further. Varying flower shapes like roundHosta blooms, spiky gladiolus, and airy baby's breath create captivating rhythms. Blending heights and forms promotes visual interest through complexity.

Another consideration is including plants that attract pollinators. Butterflies flock to brightly colored tubular blossoms of verbena, zinnias, and monarda. Bees busily harvest nectar from daisy-like echinacea, rudbeckia, and aster flowers. Moths prefer night-blooming flowers like moonflowers, datura, and flowering tobacco. Hummingbirds sip from red blooms of bee balm, fuchsia, and lobelia. Selecting pollinator favorites provides food sources that support local ecosystems. Positioning plants in dense drifts or clusters facilitates foraging. A thoughtful pollinator garden thrives with beneficial insect life.

Herbaceous plants that emit fragrance can also delight the senses in garden beds. The sweet lavender, gardenia, and jasmine perfume on the evening breeze soothes and calms. Locating them near seating areas maximizes enjoyment. When touched, fragrant roses, sweet alyssum, nicotiana, stock, and mignonette release fresh scents. Planting them along borders and paths suffuses any stroll with aroma. Night-blooming flowers like moonflowers release intensified fragrances in the cooler humidity. Contrasting day and night scents enhance the sensory experience. With strategic placement, fragrant plants infuse gardens with an enriching ambiance through natural perfume.

The intended uses of plants also guide their incorporation in beds and borders. Culinary herbs planted near kitchen doors provide convenient seasonings. Easy-access beds of salad greens offer cut-and-come-again harvest. Edible flowers like pansies, nasturtiums, and violas add nutrition and whimsy tossed in salads. Fruit-bearing shrubs around patios supply fresh berries. Fragrant antioxidant herbs promote wellness in a designated wellness garden. Plants can also create soothing spaces, block views, or attract wildlife. Considering utility maximizes function alongside floral beauty.

Repeating or contrasting blossom colors also creates appealing effects. Monochromatic beds utilizing shades like lavender hosta, astilbe, and violas make serene color echoes. Juxtaposing complementary hues like yellow coreopsis, purple salvia, and pink roses achieves vibrant results. Value contrasts like pale blue alyssum under deep blue delphiniums lends dimensional impact. Grouping analogous colors like orange, yellow, and red sunflowers and marigolds evokes warmth. Thoughtful blending and placement intensify color relationships to unify plantings. Garden beds and borders come alive when thoughtfully designed with contrasting flower forms. Tall vertical spikes of larkspur and delphiniums tower over medium daisies, coreopsis, and red valerian. Mixed heights establish layered dimensions—Intersperse low growers like sweet alyssum and creeping phlox around medium plants' feet to further build depth. Varying flower shapes like roundHosta blooms, spiky gladiolus, and airy baby's breath create captivating rhythms. Blending heights and forms promotes visual interest through complexity.

Another consideration is including plants that attract pollinators. Butterflies flock to brightly colored tubular blossoms of verbena, zinnias, and monarda. Bees busily harvest nectar from daisy-like echinacea, rudbeckia, and aster flowers. Moths prefer night-blooming flowers like moonflowers, datura, and flowering tobacco. Hummingbirds sip from red blooms of bee balm, fuchsia, and lobelia. Selecting pollinator favorites provides food sources that support local ecosystems. Positioning plants in dense drifts or clusters facilitates foraging. A thoughtful pollinator garden thrives with beneficial insect life.

Herbaceous plants that emit fragrance can also delight the senses in garden beds. The sweet perfume of lavender, gardenia, and jasmine on the evening breeze soothes and calms. Locating them near seating areas maximizes enjoyment. When touched, fragrant roses, sweet alyssum, nicotiana, stock, and mignonette release fresh scents. Planting them along borders and paths suffuses any stroll with aroma. Night-blooming flowers like moonflowers release intensified fragrances in the cooler humidity. Contrasting day and night scents enhance the sensory experience. With strategic placement, fragrant plants infuse gardens with an enriching ambiance through natural perfume.

The intended uses of plants also guide their incorporation in beds and borders. Culinary herbs planted near kitchen doors provide convenient seasonings. Easy-access beds of salad greens offer cut-and-come-again harvest. Edible flowers like pansies, nasturtiums, and violas add nutrition and whimsy tossed in salads. Fruit-bearing shrubs around patios supply fresh berries. Fragrant antioxidant herbs promote wellness in a designated wellness garden. Plants can also create soothing spaces, block views, or attract wildlife. Considering utility maximizes function alongside floral beauty.

With mindful plant choices and placement, herbaceous beds become canvases for gardeners to paint their unique vision. Traditional border designs feature graduated heights in triangular profiles for classic appeal. Formal parterres utilize geometric patterns and structural plants like boxwood hedges. Cottage gardens encourage rambling roses, hollyhocks, and self-sowing annuals for free-spirited charm. Contemporary minimalist beds display succulents and grasses in clean lines and curves. Woodland gardens incorporate ferns and shade plants under tree canopies. Herbaceous plants compose each style with personality. Tailoring plant selections to the desired aesthetic results in harmonious spaces for relaxing or entertaining. The possibilities stretch as far as the gardener's imagination.

To sustain their beauty, herbaceous borders, and beds benefit from attentive seasonal care. Spring preparation includes clearing winter debris and pruning overgrown plants to improve form. Dividing mature perennials rejuvenates them alongside propagating new plants for replenishing beds. Applying fresh mulch retains moisture and suppresses weeds. Installing stakes and trellises supports growing foliage and vines. Watering new growth prevents stress, while fertilizing provides nutrients once roots activate. These practices establish optimal conditions for the growing year ahead.

Ongoing maintenance sustains plant health for peak performance. Regular weeding reduces competition so flowers can thrive. Removing spent blooms, termed deadheading, promotes reblooming. Monitoring for pests and diseases allows early treatment. Watering during dry periods provides sufficient moisture. Staking and pruning wayward growth keeps plants looking their best. Dividing crowded clumps in fall improves air circulation and vigor. Finally, preparing for winter with mulch and protection ensures an abundant return in spring. With dedicated care centered on their needs, herbaceous plants continue gracing gardens with beauty.

Herbaceous Houseplants

Houseplants bring natural beauty indoors while purifying the air and uplifting moods. Many classic houseplants are herbaceous perennials selected for their attractive foliage and low-maintenance nature. Herbaceous houseplants thrive as easy-going companions when provided with sufficient light, water, humidity, and nutrients.

Among the most popular herbaceous houseplants are African violets with colorful rosettes of velvety leaves and dainty blooms. They prefer filtered light away from the direct sun and require evenly moist soil. Leaves can be slightly potbound but avoid waterlogged conditions. Another favorite is the cheerful Christmas cactus with segmented leaf pads. Water thoroughly when the soil dries, then provide bright light. Blooms appear in late fall and winter from flower buds that form during shortening daylight hours.

Ornamental begonias offer a diversity of leaf shapes, textures, and colorations. Rex begonias and other rhizomatous types feature dramatic painted leaves, while angel wing begonias have graceful arching stems lined with oval leaves. Most prefer filtered sunlight, reliable moisture, and humidity. Letting the soil surface dry between waterings prevents rot. Begonias thrive in terrariums and hanging baskets. Watch for powdery mildew and scale insects. Regular pruning encourages dense growth.

For cascading greenery, ivy makes a classic houseplant. Hedera helix English ivy and other Hedera species create dense trails. Keep ivy in bright indirect light, avoiding full sun exposure—water when the top several inches of soil become dry. Trim back long strands or invasive growth. Mist regularly to provide humidity and deter spider mites. Ivy's adaptability makes it ideal for shelves, mantels, and hanging containers. Other trailing houseplants include spider plants, Swedish ivy, and wandering Jews.

Flowering perennials like impatiens, hibiscus, and geraniums lend bright pops of color. Impatiens walleriana produces an abundance of small saucer-shaped blooms in white, pink, red, purple, and orange. Grow in well-drained soil and provide consistent moisture and humidity. Avoid direct sun, which can scorch leaves. Give hibiscus bright light to encourage prolific exotic flowers. Allow soil to partially dry between waterings and mist frequently. Scented geraniums offer pretty scalloped foliage and dainty clustered flowers. Grow in loamy soil in bright filtered light. Propagate through cuttings to expand the collection. Several flowering bulb plants also make excellent houseplants with seasonal blooms. Paperwhite narcissus bulbs produce dainty, fragrant white flowers even without soil if kept watered. Plant bulbs in containers with drainage holes using a well-aerated potting mix for fuller paperwhites with foliage. Provide bright indirect sunlight. Amaryllis bulbs also yield striking trumpet-shaped blossoms on tall stalks in dramatic colors like crimson, pink, white, and striped. Plant the bulb with 1/3 exposed in a container with drainage. Water sparingly until growth appears, then regularly while blooming.

Numerous herbaceous perennials feature colorful foliage that adds bright accents to indoor spaces. Caladium cultivars offer spectacular leaves in velvety red, pink, white, green, and speckled patterns resembling the exotic flora of jungles and rainforests. Provide consistently moist, rich soil and avoid full sun. Oxalis triangularis shows off vivid shamrock-like purple foliage and dainty blooms. Give bright indirect light and take care not to overwater. Peperomia species display fleshy, glossy leaves in oval, trailing, or rosette forms with dazzling textures and hues. Grow in a well-drained loam under medium to low light.

When caring for herbaceous houseplants, mind their individual preferences for light, water, and humidity. Most require bright filtered light, not direct sun. Light from a south-facing window is ideal for many flowering houseplants. Turn container plants weekly to prevent lopsided growth leaning toward light. Allow soil to partially dry between thorough waterings. Mist leaves, use pebble trays, or use a humidifier to provide 40-60% humidity, resembling their native tropical origins. Apply balanced liquid fertilizer during the growing season. Monitor for pests like spider mites, mealybugs, or aphids and treat them promptly. With proper conditions, herbaceous perennials continue thriving indoors.

The smaller size of herbaceous houseplants makes them ideal for desks and tabletops. Create engaging displays by combining houseplants with varied colors, textures, and forms. For example, pair bold striped bromeliads with delicate ferns and ivy trailing over container edges. Or collect a menagerie of small succulents for low-maintenance arrangements. The diversity of blooming and foliage options allows for endless creativity. Change out plants with the seasons for a refreshed look, utilizing outdoor specimens brought inside for winter. Houseplants kept in appropriate rooms bring natural beauty and improved well-being.

Notable Wildflowers and Their Relatives

Wildflowers hold an exalted status as jewels of nature, brightening fields and forests with their delicate, fleeting beauty. Many cultured garden plants were domesticated from these wildflower species, inherited from nature's bounty. Learning the origins of favorite flowers reconnects gardeners to ancient botanical lineages.

One of the most beloved wildflowers is the daisy. Oxeye daisy, Shasta daisy, English daisy, and many more derive from the humble wild daisy species of the Asteraceae family—their classic form of colorful ray petals surrounding golden disk florets charms meadows and garden beds alike. Wild daisies commonly symbolize innocence, loyalty, and purity across cultures. Popular garden tulips, crocuses, hyacinths, and grape hyacinths were cultivated from Eurasian wildflower bulbs of mountains and steppes. Their vivid hues and whimsical blooms now herald spring's arrival.

Brilliant poppies blanket fields and roadsides with their ephemeral silken blossoms. Various wild poppy species gave rise to beloved garden poppies, including Shirley, Iceland, and Oriental poppies. Their fleeting tissue paper blooms in fiery shades and inspires awe and delight. Lupines, foxgloves, columbines, violas, primroses, and violets also grace wildflower meadows and the perennial garden. Their inherent beauty shines, whether wild or domesticated.

Many herbs trace back to roots as wildflowers turned folk medicines before becoming kitchen staples. Wild thyme, sage, basil, parsley, dill, fennel, lemon balm, oregano, and other culinary herbs were treasured for their curative powers long before flavoring food. Gathering their healing essence connects present-day gardeners to millennia of botanical wisdom passed down. Even common dandelions and plantains are edible wildflowers with nutritive and medicinal properties. Their overlooked gifts reveal nature's boundless provision through seemingly humble plants.

Widespread little daisies gave rise to treasured garden flowers like gerbera daisies, English daisies, and the iconic Gerbera 'Estelle,' which inspired the Gerber logo. Many garden lilies, like Asiatic hybrids and Easter lilies, were bred from regional wild lily species with their trumpet blossoms nodding on meadows and hillsides. Familiar wildflowers like black-eyed Susans, California poppies, and cosmos self-sow freely in gardens, naturalizing with cheerful abandon. Ever generous, wildflowers persist in sharing their transient beauty. Many ornamental grasses trace their lineage to prairie and meadow wild grasses that add texture and graceful movement with their flowing seed heads. Prominent examples include maiden grasses, fountain grasses, pampas grass, and millet grass. Their adaptable nature allows them to thrive, from wild meadows to stylized gardens. Food crops like corn, wheat, rye, rice, and oats arose over millennia from wild grass ancestors selectively bred for grain production, without which civilization could not thrive. From graceful ornamentals to grain staples, the essential bounty of wild grasses continues sustaining human communities while beautifying uncultivated landscapes.

Even the most diminutive wildflowers inspire devotion. Dainty Lily of the Valley nodding on woodland floors enchanted past gardeners to breed the regal cultivated Lily of the Valley. Wild primroses, beloved by Victorian gardeners, were selected and bred into hybrid primrose colors expressing pure romantic fidelity. Wildflowers conserve timeless botanical wisdom passed down from nature herself through patient generations of careful stewardship by enlightened collectors and breeders. Each blossom gifts invaluable beauty, nourishment, and medicine for the discernment of those who cherish wildflowers' humble lessons.

Many cultivated flowering shrubs also find their origins as wild shrubby meadows and forest plants. Lilacs, forsythia, spirea, potentilla, and weigela were introduced from their native habitats to beautify gardens and lend privacy hedges. The Cape floral regions of South Africa yielded hardy wild pelargoniums or geraniums, which became cherished houseplants. Wherever they take root, wildflowers, and shrubs persist in sharing their gifts to elevate the human spirit and commune with nature.

Safeguarding vanishing wildflowers and their habitats is crucial to conserving botanical inheritance for future generations. Many organizations promote public education, ecological restoration, and preservation of endangered wildflowers and their environs. Conscientious gardeners can get involved by using native plants, limiting invasive species, avoiding pesticide use, and speaking out for conservation policies. Growing heirloom species that originated in the wild also honors their legacy. With care and compassion, the diverse beauty of wildflowers will continue flourishing for us all to enjoy. Their preservation immerses us in abundant living heritage.

Each wildflower's soulful beauty echoes through its descendants in the garden, recalling the generous gifts of nature. Allowing some cultivated plants to thrive outside formal beds fosters wilder spaces, speaking to an overlooked wisdom. Whatever our relationship with wildflowers and the open landscapes they illuminate, their transcendent fleeting brilliance awakens our shared inner wild spirit. Just as wildflowers freely scatter their ephemeral blossoms on untamed earth, may we also boldly bloom however we are planted, spreading beauty wherever we take root.

Chapter 8

Succulents and Cacti

Adaptations for Arid Climates

Succulents and cacti are specially adapted to thrive in hot, dry environments that would cause most other plants to wither and perish. Their unique physical and metabolic adaptations allow them to conserve precious water and survive in deserts, scrublands, steppes, and other arid regions.

One major adaptation is the ability to store water in fleshy leaves, stems, or roots. The thick, swollen tissues act as reservoirs, enabling the plants to survive long periods without rainfall. Sedums, aloes, agaves, and many Euphorbia succulents have leaves engorged with moisture-filled cells. Cacti store water in their barrel-shaped stems as well as roots. Avoiding excess transpiration keeps stored water from evaporating away. Waxy cuticles and minimal leaf surface area reduce moisture loss. Photosynthesis in succulent leaves also occurs at night when cooler temperatures prevent evaporation.

Spines, thorns, and prickly hairs protect cacti and some succulents from thirsty predators seeking the stored moisture within. Dense coatings of reflective trichomes act like mirrors to reflect sunlight and prevent overheating. Tough outer skins and bark do slow water loss while also masking the water-rich tissues. Camouflage coloration in muted greens, grays, and browns allows blending into the desert backdrop. Some stone plants even take the mimicry further, their bulbous leaves resembling pebbles. These adaptations make obtaining moisture from succulents and cacti quite challenging for would-be consumers.

In addition to water storage, succulents and cacti have evolved mechanisms to prevent excessive water loss through transpiration and respiration, even during photosynthesis. Their stomata, the pores plants use to exchange gases, remain closed during the day but open at night for low-evaporation CO2 intake. A form of photosynthesis called Crassulacean Acid Metabolism (CAM) also minimizes daytime transpiration. CAM plants take up CO2 and store it as malic acid at night, then use it for light-independent fixation during the daytime. This adaptation allows the opening of the stomata exclusively at night when temperatures are lower, reducing water lost through evaporation. The anatomy of succulents and cacti also aids water conservation. Many possess enlarged cortical cells for increased storage. Interior hollows and mucilaginous tissues help retain moisture. Taproots descend deep to access underground water, while shallow, widespread roots seize rainfall before it evaporates. Reduced or absent leaves on cacti minimize surface area for water loss through transpiration. Ribs on cactus stems allow expansion and contraction as water content fluctuates. All parts of succulent and cactus bodies evolve as reservoirs sustaining the plant through harsh dry spells.

As another mechanism to curb transpiration, many succulents and cacti reduce or modify their leaves. Leaves may be diminutive like those of stonecrop sedums or needle-thin as in ice plants. Thick waxy cuticles prevent loss of interior moisture. In some genera like Euphorbia and Echeveria, the leaves are arranged in tight rosettes to shield the meristem. Other succulents have leaves that detach easily to conserve resources. Of course, cacti possess spines rather than true leaves. The stem itself, protected by a rugged epidermis, assumes photosynthetic duties. These specialized leaves help minimize moisture loss.

Many physical and cellular adaptations equip succulents and cacti to endure scorching heat. Their spherical, cylindrical, or rosette forms have a high surface area-to-volume ratio to dissipate heat. Wax coatings and light leaf hairs reflect sunlight to maintain cooler internal temperatures. CAM photosynthesis only opens stomata at night, preventing daytime overheating. Slow growth rates mean less metabolic heat production. Dilute electrolytes in succulent cell sap withstand salinity and resist dehydration while stabilizing enzyme function. These mechanisms allow surviving temperatures over 120°F in arid habitats.

While heat adaptations prevent overheating, cold adaptations aid survival when frigid desert night temperatures plummet, and insulative layers of trichomes and epicuticular wax retain warmth. Bladders and interior spaces in fleshy tissues act as insulation. Anti-freeze proteins in cell sap prevent freeze damage. Restricting water loss also averts desiccation damage from freezing. Many desert succulents can withstand below-freezing cold through these specialized adaptations. Their anatomical and physiological evolutions allow thriving where most other vegetation would perish.

Through evolutionary time, variation and natural selection molded succulents and cacti into ideal forms to inhabit xeric environments. Their adaptive strategies prevent overheating while insulating against cold nights. Trichomes, waxy coatings, water storage tissues, and metabolic mechanisms all curb moisture loss. Spines and camouflage deter consumption of their water supply stored internally. Reduced or modified leaves further minimize transpirational loss. These complementary adaptations equip succulents and cacti to prosper where dryness excludes other plants. Their specialized structures and functions allow them to bloom in beautiful abundance across arid landscapes.

Types of Succulents and Their Care

The diversity of succulent plants provides a wealth of unique forms, textures, and colors to incorporate into gardens. Caring for the various types of succulents properly helps them thrive. The major categories include cacti along with stem, leaf, and rosette succulents.

Cacti encompass a wide range of succulent species adapted to arid climates. They store moisture in their thickened stems as well as tap roots. Modified spines known as areoles cover the stem surface. Most cacti lack leaves, instead producing colorful flowers pollinated by birds, bats, and insects. Providing excellent drainage, full sun, occasional watering, and minimal fertilizer keeps most cacti healthy.

Stem succulents store water within swollen cylindrical, columnar, or spherical stems. Euphorbiaceae contains many stem succulents, such as the pistol-shaped Euphorbia obesa. Stapeliads, a group of tropical succulents including starfish flowers, also exhibit fleshy stems. Stem succulents require fast-drying soil and prefer partial shade in hot climates. They utilize little stored water, so drought tolerance is key.

Leaf succulents encompass a diversity of rosette-forming genera like Echeveria and Sempervivum, whose succulent leaves arranged in tight clusters contain the moisture supply. Their compact growth forms conserve resources and provide protection. Many smaller leaf succulents thrive in containers and rock gardens. Leaves may take round, pointed, frilled, or oblong forms with waxy coatings. Providing leaf succulents with gritty soil, sun or partial shade, occasional deep watering, and good drainage keeps them happy.

Rosette succulents form tight ground-hugging rosettes with crowded leaves in symmetrical whorls or spirals. The low growth habit and dense leaf arrangement prevent water loss. Common rosette genera include Echeveria, Sempervivum, Aeonium, Agave, and Crassula. Hens and chicks (Sempervivum) offset spread mats of tiny rosettes resembling chicks around a larger hen. Rosette varieties add diverse shapes and textures for mixed succulent plantings. Most require gritty, porous potting soil. Take care not to over water, but soak completely when dry.

One of the most sculptural rosette succulents is the blue-gray Echeveria agavoides, with ruffled, pointed leaves forming symmetric rosettes up to 12 inches wide. This striking evergreen is native to upland regions of Central America. Another unique rosette succulent is Crassula ovata, or jade plant, with glossy oval leaves flushed pink or red in strong light. In frost-free climates, Jade plants grow as shrubs to three feet tall indoors or outdoors. Their thick trunks also store water. Slow but steady growth makes jade plants ideal for gardeners seeking robust houseplants.

Providing the proper growing conditions and care allows each type of succulent to thrive. Cacti demand the best drainage, while stem succulents require watering precisely when the soil dries. Leaf succulents enjoy partial shade in hot climates and gritty soil. Symmetric rosettes form living sculptures where their low-water adaptations provide an advantage. Getting to know the different forms and needs of succulents is key to successfully growing these resilient plants. Their diversity offers striking options, from miniature arrangements to stunning landscape specimens. Another sculptural succulent group is Aeonium, often named tree houseleeks for their branched rosettes forming clumps atop bare stems. Their arching leaves have a pinwheel shape. Most Aeonium tolerate partial shade and require fast-draining soil and occasional water. Let the soil dry between thorough soakings. Like many succulents, they thrive indoors or outdoors.

The astrophytum genus contains popular collecting cacti, including bishop's cap or Astrophytum myriostigma, named for its distinctive mitre-like shape. Zebra cactus, Astrophytum zebra, displays bold white striping over small cushions. These small cacti reach just 4-6 inches tall and flourish in containers. Provide bright light indoors and a gritty potting mix. Water deeply but allow drying between waterings.

For vivid colors, echeveria succulents deliver ruffled rosettes in intense reds, oranges, pinks, and purples. Their tight clustering conserves moisture while providing endless rosette varieties to mix and match. Echeverias thrive outdoors in mild climates. In containers, provide well-drained soil and allow drying between infrequent deep waterings. Protect from intense mid-day sun, which can scorch their fleshy leaves. Propagating echeverias from leaf cuttings yields new, colorful plants.

When growing mixed succulents, match plants with similar needs in terms of sunlight, moisture, soil, and drainage. For example, group drought-tolerant cacti and aeoniums separately from sempervivums and echeverias that require more frequent watering. Provide the same potting mix and drainage strategies to compatible groupings. A gravel or sand top dressing blends arrangements while stabilizing soil moisture. Allow each type of succulent to guide its own care through observation. This prevents under or overwatering mismatched plants. Soon, their unique forms and hues will merge into living art.

Caring for any succulent requires paying close attention to its needs. Look for signs like wrinkling leaves or drooping, which indicate under-watering. Overwatering may cause leaves to turn yellow or drop. Noting the conditions where particular varieties thrive and then replicating those prevents most issues. Most succulents are happy with fast drainage, granular soil, infrequent deep soaking, and protective sunshine. Avoiding temperature extremes and sudden changes in care protects sensitive species. With a nurturing hand, succulents unfurl intricate beauty even in difficult conditions.

Cactus Diversity and Identification

The cactus family, Cactaceae, contains over 2,000 diverse species adapted to arid habitats across the Americas. Cacti range from tiny button-like cacti under an inch tall to towering columnar giants over 60 feet. While all cacti share some key adaptations like water storage tissues and spines, their many unique forms captivate botanists and collectors.

One major grouping includes globular, cylindrical, and barrel cacti with rounded profiles. This category encompasses popular genera like Ferocactus, Echinocactus, and Mammillaria. These cacti often form dense clusters of short columns covered in spines and ribs. Their spherical shapes offer a high surface area-to-volume ratio to dissipate heat. Many globular cacti produce large and beautifully intricate flowers. Their sizes range from small hairy pincushions to massive barrel cacti weighing hundreds of pounds.

Columnar cacti exhibit upturned branches resembling candelabras, giving rise to names like swordpear, totem pole, and candelabra cactus. Genera include Cereus, Cleistocactus, and Oreocereus, some with branches exceeding 30 feet. Ridges along their stems expand and contract to store water. They offer a spectacle of vertical lines for xeric landscape gardens. Columnar cacti thrive where summer rainfall permits their large forms. Some are night-blooming with exquisitely scented flowers pollinated by bats and moths.

The Opuntia subfamily contains prickly pears and chollas recognizable by their flattened, segmented pads. They reliably flower in an array of colors. Upright or rounded pads detaching easily make Opuntia prone to propagation and spread. Their modified spines (glochids) also readily attach to passersby to disperse segments. Prickly pears like Engelmann's prickly pear tolerate a range of climates while providing delicious edible fruits. Jumping chollas earned their name from detached stems that cling to passing animals, giving the illusion of jumping. Though often considered a nuisance, opuntias' remarkable adaptations and beauty highlight cactus family diversity. The epiphyllum genus, also called orchid cactus, comprises jungle cacti with flattened stems forming cascading chains of leaf-like segments. Brilliant flowers in red, orange, pink, and white make epiphyllum popular as hanging basket houseplants. They require light shade to avoid scorching their thin stems, excellent drainage, and minimal watering. Though epiphytic in origin, commercial hybrids thrive potted in peat-based soil. Supportive trellising helps encourage the elongated stems as they grow.

Additional diverse growth forms characterize numerous cactus genera. Rhipsalis species trail-like vines with cylindrical stems adapted to absorbing moisture and nutrients as epiphytes in tropical forests. Their small berries offer food for birds that then disperse the seeds. Discocactus includes low-growing species with flattened spherical tops. They form dense clusters emitting rings of flowers in shades of pink, fuchsia, yellow, and red. Many grow only a few inches tall but may slowly reach over one foot in diameter given years to mature.

Of course, no discussion of cacti is complete without mentioning the iconic saguaro cactus. These majestic pillars exceed 45 feet in height and symbolize the landscapes of the Sonoran Desert. Waxy ribs expand to store up to 200 gallons of water from brief summer rains. The saguaro's lifetime stretches up to 200 years, with reproduction starting around 75 years of age. Their night-blooming waxy white flowers open just one night before withering in the daytime heat. Saguaros are adapted to extremely arid conditions, making them an iconic part of the desert.

With such incredible diversity across genera and species, identifying cacti takes practice. Examining stem characteristics provides clues. The presence of ribs, tubercles, or segmentation, along with spine formation, helps reveal groupings. Flower traits like size, color, bloom time, and placement also aid identification. Referencing location and habitat offers additional insights, as epiphytic jungle cacti and desert cacti vary enormously. Seeking expert guidance from local gardens, books, and online resources facilitates accurate cactus identification. Unraveling their unique adaptations captivates botanists worldwide.

While often associated with desert environments, cacti inhabit diverse regions. Tropical forests nurture epiphytic cacti high in tree canopies. Coastal Brazilian resting as support expansive golden ball cacti carpeting sandy soils where moisture persists. Hardy opuntias extend north into Canada. Located in Chile, the Atacama Desert is the driest non-polar desert on Earth. It still sustains extensive cactus vegetation. Even cool alpine environments foster rosette-forming cacti. Identifying cacti by region provides environmental clues aiding identification. Tracking down the origins of mystery specimens helps reveal their secrets. Each cactus carries a story of generational change unfolding under unique pressures.

Growing Succulents and Cacti Indoors and Outdoors

The drought-adapted nature of succulents and cacti makes them ideal easy-care indoor plants. Providing suitable growing conditions both indoors and out allows these sculptural desert plants to thrive. Matching natural environmental preferences facilitates success.

Indoors, succulents, and cacti require locations with abundant sunlight from southern or western windows. Supplemental artificial lighting benefits plants situated in darker spots. Soilless potting mixes work well to offer fast drainage critical for preventing root rot. Clay or terra cotta planters also improve drainage while wicking away excess moisture. Since most succulents store water in leaves, stems, or roots, they require infrequent watering. Allow soil to fully dry between deeper soakings.

During winter, when growth slows, succulents and cacti may only need monthly watering. Take care not to overwater, as soggy soil quickly leads to rotting. Adding gravel, sand, or perlite improves soil aeration and drainage to prevent moisture buildup. Drainage trays catch overflow water. Terracotta pots absorb excess liquid through porous walls. Matching soil and containers prevents wet conditions.

A diversity of succulents and cacti thrive as houseplants. Hens and chicks (Sempervivum) offset freely to form mats of rosettes ideal for containers. Watch chain plant (Crassula perforata) trails attractively with tiny stacked leaves. Small barrel cacti and mamillaria stay compact on sunny windowsills. Jade plants (Crassula ovata) tolerate lower light while showing off glossy oval leaves. Flowering types like holiday cactus (Schlumbergera) and African milk tree (Euphorbia trigona) display colorful seasonal blooms.

Outdoors, cacti, and succulents require similar conditions of excellent drainage and ample sunlight. For in-ground planting, amending native soil with extra pumice, gravel, or sand creates a suitable gritty texture. Raised beds prevent waterlogged conditions in wet climates. Leave adequate space between plants to allow air circulation and avoid fungal issues. Mulching helps insulate roots while stabilizing soil moisture and humidity. Locate beds in full sun exposures. In very hot regions, light afternoon shade prevents scorching. Heat and sunlight aid growth.

For container culture outdoors, clay and concrete planters work well alongside traditional terra cotta pots. Ensure drainage holes allow excess water to evacuate the container. Top dressings of mineral grit stabilize moisture levels—group pots together on gravel beds for excellent drainage. Maintain spacing between containers to prevent fungal growth. As with indoor care, allow soils to dry completely before deep watering. Extended drought will not harm most succulents and cacti. Their adaptations allow for tolerating low water dormancy.

Both indoor and outdoor succulents benefit from occasional fertilizing during the active growing season. Use a balanced dilute fertilizer every 2-3 months. Avoid overfertilizing, as succulents store extra nutrients, which can burn the plant. Cease feeding in fall and winter when entering dormancy. Removing dead leaves and flower stems keeps plants looking tidy. Pruning damaged or rotting sections also improves health. Succulents and cacti adapt well to diverse environments with proper siting, soils, and seasonal care. When growing succulents and cacti outdoors, climate considerations guide appropriate plant selections. Tropical cacti like Christmas cactus and orchid cactus require warm, frost-free regions. Hardier opuntias and prickly pears withstand brief freezing. High-elevation succulents prefer cool summer nights. Choosing plants matched to regional temperatures prevents losses.

In arid climates, supplemental irrigation maintains health. Relying solely on rainfall proves inadequate in most deserts. Careful watering through the hottest, driest months sustains plants between rainy periods. Monitor for signs of shriveled or wrinkled leaves indicating thirst. Even the most drought-hardy cacti benefit from occasional deep soakings in drought. Provide extra water to root zones instead of overhead watering, which can scorch tender tissues.

Humid climates make fungal diseases a challenge for succulents and cacti. Ensuring sharp drainage prevents crown and root rot. Allowing air circulation around plants reduces moisture accumulation. Top dressings like gravel or sand minimize soil moisture at the base. Positioning pots on wire racks or feet elevates containers above wet surfaces. Treat any fungal infections promptly to avoid spreading. With proactive care, succulents and cacti adapt and thrive outside of their native arid habitats.

Colder winters require seasonal preparation in areas with freezing temperatures. Gradually reducing watering in fall hardens off plants and minimizes cell damage when frozen. Covering containers with insulation like burlap aids smaller plants. Popular cold-hardy cacti like prickly pear may endure brief freezes with no protection needed. Move fragile jungle cacti and succulents indoors before frost hits. A bright, sunny window sustains growth for overwintering houseplants.

For in-ground specimens in colder zones, providing winter mulch stabilizes soil temperatures. Remove mulch in spring to avoid excess moisture against the plant base. Positioning rocks, mounds of soil, and burlap wrappings shelter root zones and crowns. Avoid fertilizing late in the year, as succulents should enter dormancy without active growth. With seasonally appropriate adaptations, cacti and succulents grace gardens year-round outside their native ranges.

Gardeners in challenging climates can also employ creative solutions like cold frames, greenhouses, and raised beds for added winter insulation. Opt for cold-tolerant cacti and succulents when selecting outdoor specimens. Sturdy opuntias withstand a wider range of conditions than tropical euphorbias. With knowledge of plant hardiness zones, microclimates, and seasonal care, cacti, and succulents diversify gardens across varied regions. Their beauty persists when thoughtfully sited and cared for appropriately throughout the annual weather cycle.

Uses of Succulents and Cacti

Beyond their visual appeal, succulents and cacti provide numerous practical uses. Their diversity lends itself to diverse applications from ornamental plants, cuisine, fencing, and traditional medicine. Throughout history, human societies have developed specialized uses for succulent plants based on local species available.

The most ubiquitous use of succulents is in gardens and containers for ornamental purposes. Their sculptural shapes, textures, and coloring make succulents ideal accent plants. Hens and chicks, agaves, aloes, echeverias, and sedums add contrast and structure among flowering plants. Prickly pears, barrels, and mamillaria cacti make striking statement pieces. Cascading succulents like burro tail or string of pearls spill gracefully from hanging pots. The trend towards waterwise landscaping has popularized succulents for their drought tolerance. Creative succulent walls, beds, and sculptures utilize succulents as living works of art.

Various edible succulent species provide food, drink, and sweeteners. Prickly pear and related opuntia cactus pads, also called nopales, are common ingredients in Mexican cuisine with their mucilaginous texture. The ruby red prickly pear fruits offer a sweet, tangy flavor, fresh or as agua fresca drinks, candies, jams, and jellies. Dragon fruit grows on climbing cacti and bears edible pitaya fruits. The aloe vera plant contains gel to soothe burns, wounds, and skin irritation. Extracting and processing agave juice creates sweet nectar and tequila liquor. Many cultures have developed culinary uses for local succulents.

The fiber, thorns, and morphology of some succulents also lend themselves to practical uses like fencing, binding, and sewing: leggy prickly pear and organ pipe cactus segments piece together into living fences and property borders. Agave leaves yield fibers historically twisted into cordage, nets, and cloth. Their sharp terminal spines functioned as needles. Cleaver hooks secure cut pads and fruits during foraging. Columnar cacti form impenetrable hedges and barriers. Creative artisans continue building furniture, baskets, textiles, and crafts from succulent raw materials.

Indigenous cultures worldwide developed traditional plant-based medicines utilizing succulents. Aloe vera sap heals skin, reduces inflammation, and relieves burns. Fermented agave sap makes an antiseptic wound wash. Splitting clubs cacti release disinfecting pulp. Prickly pear extracts exhibit antiviral, antioxidant, and anti-inflammatory properties. Dragon fruit extracts may support immunity and heart health. Traditional healing arts recognized the curative gifts within arid-adapted succulents. Some remedies now carry into modern alternative medicine systems. The adaptations that allow succulents and cacti to thrive in arid environments also make them ideal plants for green roofs, walls, and landscapes in modern times. Their shallow root systems and low water needs allow succulent plantings on shallow soil depths. CAM photosynthesis minimizes water loss, reducing irrigation demands. Fleshy leaves stems, and roots store reserves that allow for surviving drought. These attributes make succulents sustainable choices for green infrastructure, residential landscaping, and public parks in dry regions.

In green roofs, sedums and sempervivums form drought-tolerant mats that withstand the harsh growing conditions on rooftops. The carpeting foliage adds insulation, reducing stormwater runoff and cooling underlying buildings through evapotranspiration—planted walls featuring cascading succulents like a string of pearls or desert trumpets vertically garden indoor and outdoor spaces—the minimal soil depths required broadening installation options. Succulent plantings beautify urban areas with minimal irrigation and maintenance needs once established.

Waterwise gardens and xeriscaping utilize hardy succulents and cacti in place of thirsty lawns and plantings. Fleshy agaves, aloes, and euphorbias combine with ornamental gravel mulch and boulders for ultra-low water landscaping. Once adopted, many succulents thrive solely on rainfall in dry regions. Their sculptural forms make succulents ideal focal points within desert garden designs. Public parks and botanic gardens in arid climates increasingly feature arid-adapted borders and beds. Succulents demonstrate that beautiful, sustainable landscapes are possible even with scarce precipitation.

The horticultural industry selectively breeds hundreds of new succulent cultivars to meet consumer demand. New sizes, colors, textures, and plant forms offer ever-greater possibilities. Miniature succulents work in terrariums and fairy gardens while giant agaves make dramatic specimens. Contrasting textures and colors allow for striking mixed plantings. Scientists also research disease-resistant, cold-hardy varieties to expand growing regions. Bioengineering may yield succulents tailored for landscaping, green roofs, or indoor air purification. Ongoing innovations will likely open additional applications suited to succulents' unique adaptations and environmental benefits.

Rare and Endangered Desert Plants

Many extraordinary succulents and cacti face endangerment in the wild due to climate change, habitat loss, poaching, livestock grazing, and other threats. As natural habitats degrade, conserving these rare desert jewels becomes critical. Several iconic and unusual species are now on the verge of extinction.

Florida's state cactus, the prickly apple cactus, exhibits brilliant fuchsia flowers following summer rains. Just two small populations remain in the Florida Keys due to coastal development and illegal collection. Its limited habitat and declining numbers classify it as endangered. Ongoing conservation efforts aim to reintroduce cultivated specimens to protect and preserve lands.

The rare Marojejya darianii inhabits a single remote desert patch of southwestern Madagascar. This massive endangered succulent glows neon green before producing towering yellow-spired blooms. Its isolated shale terrain shelters just hundreds of plants. Mining and mineral exploration, along with climate shifts, remain serious threats. However, its novelty has drawn attention and propagation efforts to protect the unique Marojejya.

Africa's bizarre elephant-foot yam evokes its common name with a massive subterranean caudex that can weigh over 100 pounds. This unusual succulent pumps out huge umbrella-like leaves to quickly collect rainfall before annual dormancy. Rampant overharvesting for traditional medicine has decimated wild populations, now listed as vulnerable. Elephant-foot yam requires legal cultivation practices to reduce dangerous poaching levels.

The regal Queen Victoria agave hails from central Mexico's dry forests. Mature plants form a majestic rosette up to six feet wide crowned by a tall bloom spike before dying. Deforestation severely reduced its arid habitat and remaining numbers. Continued clearing for farming and grazing without protective measures could soon drive this vulnerable species to extinction. However, increased propagation and habitat restoration offer hope.

Poaching has also devastated the wild populations of many prized peyote cacti like Lophophora williamsii. Indigenous groups traditionally use this rare hallucinogenic cactus in spiritual ceremonies. Rampant illegal collecting for illicit drug trade now threatens these unusual spineless cacti. Trade restrictions, anti-poaching patrols, and seed banking may preserve peyote's limited remaining habitats across the desert borderlands of Mexico and Texas. The remote Socotra archipelago off Yemen's coast hosts an array of ancient endemic succulents found nowhere else on Earth. The flagship dragon's blood tree exhibits umbrella-shaped branches with red sap. Just a few hundred remain due to livestock overgrazing. The giant cucumber tree Dionysia mirabilis with swollen water-storing bases once proliferated on Socotra but now nears extinction in the wild.

Rampant development for tourism infrastructure and overharvesting further threaten dozens more of Socotra's uniquely adapted succulents. Conservation groups now work to propagate and reintroduce rare dragon's blood trees while promoting sustainable ecotourism and botanic research to preserve these ancient island relics.

South Africa's desert succulent flora faces a grave decline as well. Many aloe species, like the regal Aloe pillansii, suffered massive losses from overcollection for the horticultural trade before protection efforts began. Others contend with habitat fragmentation, invasive plants, and climate change pressures. Dozens of South African aloe species now cling to endangered or vulnerable status, reliant on cultivation, sustainable propagation, and habitat management to offer hope.

Even widespread genera like Echeveria succulents contain rare species. Echeveria elegans exhibits dark green rosettes blushed with pink, native to a small range in Mexico's Sierra Madre mountains. Habitat loss renders its limited numbers endangered. Careful cultivation and reintroduction can prevent extinction. Other echeverias face similar fates due to agricultural conversion and overharvesting.

Some cacti even stand on the brink of vanishing forever. The diminutive star cactus endemic to Cuba survives only in a westerly settlement, Boquerón. Just 500 individuals remain in the wild due to poaching and grazing. These lone remnants now gain government protection, but survival remains tenuous even with propagation attempts. Without intervention, this species could soon be lost.

While habitat preservation can secure wild succulents, home cultivation also carries importance. Responsible propagation generates specimens for restoration projects while reducing poaching pressures. Sharing rare plants among collectors ensures genetic diversity. Botanic gardens showcase threatened species as ambassadors for their kin. We all bear responsibility for stemming the loss of these singular desert treasures. From conservation initiatives to mindful stewardship, our actions honor the venerable legacy encoded within Earth's most tenacious dryland survivors.

Closing Remarks:

As we reach the conclusion of our journey through the expansive diversity of the plant kingdom, one truth stands clear: Plants are the foundation of all life on Earth. From towering ancient redwoods to tiny mosses, plants nourish, shelter, heal, and sustain us. Their beauty inspires our cultures. Photosynthesis forms the basis of every food chain while providing the oxygen that animates our world. Our future and plants' future remain inextricably intertwined.

Understanding plants leads us better to understand ourselves and our place within nature's web. The more we learn about plants, the more fascinated we become by life's incredible complexity. Our human relationship with plants stretches back to our origins. Like us, plants inhabit this planet together, shaping the environment and each other over eons through intricately interwoven lives. At a time when ecological balance hangs in precarious uncertainty, plants call to us more urgently than ever. Their fragile diversity encodes wisdom passed down since the dawn of terrestrial life. Will we listen and act to protect our green kindred? The answer will define the destiny of life on Earth.

But knowledge alone does not suffice. As we have seen, diverse cultures honor plants through principles of deep interconnection and mutual care. Living, working, and creating in partnership with plants weaves meaning and vitality. Beyond preserving biodiversity, true stewardship recognizes the intrinsic value within each unique organism we are blessed to share this world with. May the gifts gleaned here inspire readers to tend new relationships with the miraculous plants enriching our lives each day. As we cultivate understanding and compassion for all our plant kin, we build a just, sustainable, and sacred home. Together, we walk as guardians of an ancient green heritage germinating the future.

www.ingramcontent.com/pod-product-compliance
Lightning Source LLC
LaVergne TN
LVHW020016121224
798917LV00039B/1182

9789493212404